Eurochild

First published in 2003 by

Eurochild International Project
Tigh Filí
Thompson House
MacCurtain Street
Cork, Ireland
Phone: 353 21 450 9274
Fax: 353 21 455 1617
e-mail: admin@cwpc.ie
Website: www.tighfili.com

British Library Cataloguing in Publication Data
ISBN 0 949010 95 2

The use of ISBN number was kindly donated by Bradshaw Books
Cover art by Éanna Ó Corragáin
Cover design by Antoine Sterkendries
Typeset and Layout by the Eurochild Team
Printed and Bound by Betaprint, Ireland

Eurochild International Festival is sponsored by Cork City of Culture 2005

Eurochild

2 0 0 3

edited by
Declan Barron

Eurochild International Project
Cork, Ireland

Acknowledgements

We received thousands of entries for *Eurochild 2003* fom Ireland and all over Europe so I would like to thank and congratulate each and every child for all their effort and creativity. This edition would not have been completed without the help of Eurochild International Project Team; thanks to my colleagues Kate O'Sullivan for typesetting, Antoine Sterkendries for cover design, Linda Benmalek and Azeline Le Quillec for translations and European correspondence and also to Ferdia Ó Corragáin and Sasha Palkova for translations. My thanks to Claire Horgan, and Managing Editor Liz Willows. Finally, thank you Máire Bradshaw.

Poetry

V

2003 eurochild

VI

2003 *eurochild*

2003 eurochild

VIII

2003 eurochild

X

Artwork

2003 eurochild

XII

2003 *eurochild*

Foreword

Depuis 1988 l'association Euro Ecole a pour objectif de développer auprés des jeunes enfants l'ideé d'une identité européenne construite á partir de la diversité culturelle, dans le respect des différences. Diverses actions sont menées pour inciter les enfants á communiquer, se recontrer, élaborer et participer á des projects communs.

Eurochild fait partie de ces projets qui enthousiasment les enfants et les enseignants. Cette année, afin d'aider les enfants á composer leurs poémes les enseignants ont pu participé á une formation sur la création poétique, organisée par Euro Ecole.

Que cette édition 2003 d'Euro Ecole et Eurochild, que tous les poémes écrits par ces enfants Européens soient autant de messages de paix pour l'Europe et pour la terre entiére.

Isabelle Brondy
Présidente d'Euro Ecole

2003

3rd & 4th Class Enniscrone NS, Sligo
Brown Bull of Cooley 1

I am delighted to see contributions from so many countries: France, Georgia, Wales, Spain, Portugal, Germany, Finland, Czech Republic, Bulgaria, Malta and Ireland. At a time when our awareness of our place on the World stage has been heightened by our achievements, it is particularly heartening to see how our children's awareness of their equal partnership on the European stage can be enhanced through involvement in projects such as *Eurochild*.

One of the main objectives of the National Children's Strategy, which informs all Government policy on children, is that children shall be given a voice and the their voices will be heard: as a Government we endeavour to do this through such initiatives as Dáil nÓg and through participation in international events such as the U.N. Assembly on Children. Projects such as *Eurochild* are equally important, providing as they do an outlet for children's creative voices, allowing children to explore the issues and to develop the self-belief that comes from our encouraging and nurturing their individuality. All of this will help us to build confidence in our children into the future: confidence in their ability to express themselves, confidence in our willingness to hear what they have to say and confidence in their role as citizens not just of their community, but of their country and of Europe.

I am delighted to acknowledge the importance of Cork in this process, in encouraging the development of *Eurochild* as a completely child-centred event in Cork's cultural calendar and I am particularly pleased to note that one of the long term objectives of the 'Eurochild project is to have a "Eurochild International Festival" in Cork as part of the 'European City of Culture' celebrations in 2005.

I extend my congratulations to you all once again and I wish you every success.

Michaél Martin
Minister for Health and Children.

2003 *eurochild*

3rd & 4th Class Enniscrone NS, Sligo
Brown Bull of Cooley 2

Introduction

I feel very honoured to be invited to write this introduction to *Eurochild 2003*. As a former teacher I have always been conscious of the creativity, the openness and moral bravery, of childhood and youth.

The poems and artwork in this book are a testament to the lyrical richness of our European world. For many years Tigh Fílí in Cork and Euro Ecole in Nantes have worked together to build and to celebrate a common imaginative home. As Isabelle Brondy wrote in 2001 'Eurochild et Euro Ecole defendant l'idee d'une unite dans la diversite...' Differences of nationality, of race and colour, simply melt away as children, teachers and editors discover their common human heritage. Poems like Sara Cotter's 'My Nana', Shauna Hogan's 'The Princess' Rescue' and Joanna Claxton's 'Feelings' restore us immediately to the worlds of myth, storytelling and love. Other poems, such as Ross Kiely's 'Black Bird' remind us of one of the most pressing questions of the present era - the question of our environment and how it can be protected. Paula Cashel's 'Special Olympics' with its topical, up-to-the-minute theme, does remind us of the wonderful event planned in Ireland for the summer of 2003. Her words embody the spirit of the Special Olympics:

> They train really hard,
> Golf, basketball, Tennis too,
> And spend a long time wishing
> For their dreams to come true.

Inspired by those wonderful Special Olympics, we will be settling down in Cork to plan (and train really hard!) for another brilliant international event: I mean our own European Capital of Culture: Cork 2005. Cork in 2005 will be full of the best memories and the best cultural activity. I take this opportunity to welcome everyone to this year of arts and community, of music, theatre and literature. There will be many challenging, informative and entertaining projects for children and youth; it is our expectation that the *Eurochild* will be a vibrant and colourful presence in 2005.

In the meantime, let me congratulate each individual involved in the production of this book - every young author, every young artist, every teacher and editor. This is a beautiful work; it is both entertaining and thought-provoking. Enjoy the beauty and openness, as well as the sense of Europe-wide community, in these gifted pages.

John Kennedy,
Director, Cork City of Culture 2005

2003 eurochild

3rd & 4th Class Enniscrone NS, Sligo
Brown Bull of Cooley 3

Black Bird

My life is an uninterrupted routine
Living on the rugged green cliffs,
Soaring and diving for fish in the sea,
Cool air ruffling my white velvet feathers.

Just one tanker, rolling on a rough sea
The high waves battering its hull,
Leaning to its side it spills its blackness.
So angry and afraid at one more
Eco disaster!

This oil blinds me like a tight chain
I cannot see the other birds or the
bright blue sky.
I want to fly but the black tar ties me down,
In my mind I am soaring...
I never wanted to be a black bird.

Black Bird: Ross Kiely
Art: Ross Kiely

eurochild
2003

Being Silly

Don't be silly so...
Don't flush your shoe down the loo
Don't lock your granny in the Zoo
Don't put suncream on the cat
Don't keep your pencils in your hat
Don't put custard on your meat
Don't write your homework with your feet
You're only being silly.

Being Silly: Killian Schäfer
Art: Ellen Moynihan

I Have Learned

Mostly I have learned
to talk in my head,
tell myself
It's not me, I'm alright -
they're the idiots, the misfits.
Eventually it sinks in.

I'm getting tougher inside.
It's working.
Just don't give in.

Try anything, anything.
But don't let them win.

2003 eurochild

I Have Learned: Shane Ryan

The World Today

People smoke, people drink
these people just don't think
if they only tried to quit
they'd be more healthy
they'd be more fit.

Their friends tell them every day
but they just shout "Go away"!
If they only tried to quit
their lives might brighten up a bit.

eurochild
2003

The World Today: David Aherne
Art: Muna Aptamohyeba

Sunset

Slowly the strong sun sets
Leaving a path of light
Like a snail's trail of slime
Suddenly it disappears out of sight
Until it rises the next day.

Crisis

Plane
Crashes
In New York
Population
Drops!!!

2003 eurochild

Sunset: Mark O'Driscoll
Crisis: David O'Driscoll

The Colours of Wales

The red fiery dragon soaring through a clear blue sky.
The green grass dancing in an open field.
These are colours of Wales.
The white baby lambs leaping through lush green fields.
The vast brown forests creeping high in small valleys.
These are colours of Wales.
The yellow daffodils swaying slowly in a cool breeze on mountain tops.
The clear blue lake glistening in the moonlight.
These are colours of Wales.
The gloomy grey of clouds creeping across a dark sky ready to rain.
The black coal resting in a dense dark coal mine.
These are colours of Wales.

The Colours of Wales: James Longville

The Four Seasons

The breeze rustles leaves
Baby lambs enter the world
Spring is beautiful

The suns rays shine down
The beach is swarming with people
Summer is scorching

Leaves swiftly drift down
They crinkle high in the trees
Leaves swirl in Autumn

All the flowers die
They are withering away
Winter brings presents

The Four Seasons: Owen Stenner Matthews & Matthew Peatie

2003 eurochild

Everlasting Traffic Jam

I hate long traffic jams.
And all sorts of noises.
Roaring like fierce lions.
Engines throbbing and revving.
Sending vibrations
up my stomach.
A strong stinking
smell of fuel.
Reminding me of
a bubbling cauldron.
Gears grating.
Like wild cats.
Breaks grinding.
Like Grandpa's false teeth.
Traffic lights flashing.
Like lightening lashing.
Coaches creeping slowly.
Like starving alligators.
I am stuck in the traffic jam.
Longing to go home before it's too late.

2003 *eurochild*

Everlasting Traffic Jam: Steve Sammut Alessi
Art: Stacey Gallagher

Fishing

Today it is a good wet day
I think I will go fishing
I will catch something for the tea
My mammy she is wishing.

I get my gear all ready
Must not forget my rod
Off I go to meet my friend
He wants to catch some cod.

Down to the water's edge we go
We hop into the boat
It's a little chilly on the lake,
I think I'll wear a coat.

2003 eurochild

Fishing: Ciarán Seoige

A Flower

Of all God's creations big or small
The flower is for me the loveliest of them all
In red, white, yellow or of a green colour
Of different hues you can find a flower.

In fields and in gardens they grow and abound
If ever you wanted some you surely have found.
With grace and with beauty they grow in the wild
They mirror God's wonder, His might and His light.

In churches and homes for the old and the young
Flowers are there to express joy and love.
On birthdays, feasts and for every event
No better present can you ever get

Flowers don't cost too much money
And yet they're so precious more than honey
Of life's greatest pleasures for me to enjoy
Is to gaze at a flower with love and with awe.

A Flower: Karl Meli
Art: Karolina Ludvikova

My Family

There are six of us in our house
And Dad and Mam makes eight
Sometimes it's cramped and crowded
But most of the time it's great

We play all kinds of football
Gaelic, rugby and soccer too
It can be rough and tumble
And we are often black and blue

At cards you couldn't watch them
As they argue about the count
Did someone stick the dealer
Or not stake the right amount

When someone's gear goes missing
It can end up in a row
I could tell you lots of stories
But that's all I'll say for now

The fact that I'm the youngest
Can be good as well as bad
But still I'm very grateful
For all the fun we've had.

2003 eurochild

My Family: Ciarán McCormack

Where Books Take Me

Books take me to a land afar,
A land far, far away.
I have lots of fun
And I don't have a care
While I'm there
Some books take me to New York City
Others to Australia or Spain
I met a dragon once
In a land far, far away

Winter

Winter is lots of fun,
I made a snowman with my Mum,
No nice flowers or apples grow,
The hedgehog is hibernating from the snow,
End of autumn, waiting for spring,
Rainbow in the sky is a beautiful thing.

2003 eurochild

Where Books Take Me: Shauna McGowan
Winter: Sorcha Thomas

My Mum

My Mum smiles slowly
as if you are watching the sun set;
she has bushy brown curls
that are long to her shoulders.
My Mum has beautiful,
dazzling brown eyes
as if they were made of the chocolate
she simply adores;
massages especially when she's tired.
My Mum is a wonderful, unique cook
all her recipes taste perfect.
My favorite recipe of my Mum's
is chocolate eclairs -
rich cream pastry!

My Mum: Edward G. Zammit
Art: Breda Dwyer

A School

Behold! A school am I.
Everyday I am used except Saturday and Sunday
I have a lot of children and teachers,
I am afraid when the children and teachers are gone,
I am not the only school around.

The Foot

Hairy foot, hairy foot
Hairy, hairy foot
I like the way you stay on the ground
Wiggling your five toes.

A School: Dylan Magee
The Foot: Miranda Casey

No More School

The bell rang accompanied
by an eruption of cheers.
This is the tradition for the
past hundred years,
They picked up their bags and
away they did run. Smiles on their
faces under a hot baking sun.
"We're as free as the wind" they
said as they grinned. "Tonight"
they exclaimed "we will get all
        our books and set them aflame"
             and also tonight after books
                were destroyed they'd have a
                  great party and play with
                    their toys.

2003 eurochild

No More School: Adrienne McManus
Art: Aaron Carroll

Around Us

I walked out to my garden
Sat down on my chair
I could not believe what
God had left there
The scenery, the wild life
Were lovely and fair
If only we'd stop
And sometimes stare.

Around Us: Shona Cawley
Art: Sarah Ryan

Madness

Madness is the colour red
It tastes like burnt toast
And smells like a room of smoke
It looks like the devil
And sounds like horror music
It feels rock rock solid

My Old Porsche 911

When I woke up I thought I was in Heaven
When I laid my eyes on my Porsche 911,
I felt so excited that I could not wait
to jump right in and pedal it straight.
But all the same it came to an end
and I said goodbye to my little old friend
All of a sudden I could not sit in my Porsche 911,
I wouldn't fit.

Madness: Sinéad Gilligan
My Old Porsche 911: Matthew Finn

Green is...

Green is the colour of my sparkly eyes.
It is the colour of green beans
and ripe juicy pears.

Green is the colour of swaying grass.
It is the colour of tall trees
and glistening dragon flies

Green is the colour of summer insects.
It is the colour of round peas
and seaweed in the blue sea.

2003 eurochild

Green is: Sophie Austin

Meereshymme

Wenn es stürmt von Norden her,
peitscht der Wind scharf übers Meer,
drückt das Wasser an den Strand,
aus trockenem-wird nasser Sand.
Die Wellen brechen sich am Riff,
oder donnern bis ans Kliff,
es brodelt, schäumt, der Spuk hört auf,
das Leben nimmt den alten Lauf.

Wenn die Abendzeit beginnt,
die Sonne langsam niedersinkt,
als Feuerball im Meer verschwindet,
woanders dann den Tag verkündet,
dann denkt man, es wird ewige Nacht,
das Meer hat der Sonne den Garaus gemacht.
Doch es ist nicht viel passiert,
die Sonne kommt, wenn's Morgen wird.

Am Strand die Möwen ziehen Kreise,
in den Bäumen raschelt 's leise.
Ein Bernstein wird an Land gespült,
wo 'n Fuchs die Schwalbeneier stiehlt.
Im Wasser springt ein Buckelwal,
der Meeresgrund ist auch nicht kahl,
ohne Wasser gäb's kein Leben,
und Menschen würd' es auch nicht geben.

Meereshymme: Thomas Faelligen & Vladimir Volinschi

2003 eurochild

Christmas

Christmas is near
It only comes once a year,
What I want for Christmas is a cell phone
So I can ring my friends all on my own.

Bond doesn't do a mission on Christmas Day
He works his charm only in May,
I hate giving presents in the Christmas Season
I really think there is no reason.

The girls love me, they think I'm heaven
That is why they call me 007,
The poem is about to end
It's around the next bend.

Yippee! Another verse of mine
Now I'll tell you how I learn my lines,
I think it is fair to say
I look great in *Die Another Day*.

eurochild
2003

Christmas: Matthew Roche
Art: Sorcha Thomas

Christmas

As I stand there, with posters of me, everywhere,
Now I know, I don't want to go,
I'm scared and I'm worried,
Then a woman who's hurried,
Comes and takes me away,
But I desperately want to stay.

I am taken to a strange place,
I don't want to be here at all,
I am taken out of my case,
Then wrapped in a ball,
It's dark and scary, I am very wary,
Where am I at all?

A few weeks later, I hear a loud sound,
I am taken from my paper,
Then dropped to the ground,
I look around and what do I see?
A boy that doesn't want to play with me.

2003 eurochild

Christmas: Stephan Costello
Art: Sorcha Thomas

Christmas

Plastic Santa neon light
windows filled with merchandise,
the lists of gadgets and toys
on their way for the girls and boys.

The same old films that we have seen
trees that are forever green,
Scrooge is gone
and nobody is mean.

It seems we all lost sight of
the memory of the Christmas night,
Christ child laid in
a bed of hay
the true meaning
of Christmas day,
His only
light the stars above him.

2003 eurochild

Christmas: James Peppard

A Robin's Christmas

I notice families cuddled up in their homes
watching T.V. or eating turkey off thebone.

A blanket of snow is all I can see
except a ranger cutting down a tree,
I land on the snow and what do I see
a bright white cat following me.

I know one thing I'm not spending
Christmas in a cat's tummy.

I fly up a tree,
feeling safe and free,
but then I realised that cats can climb trees.

Within a moment he swiped for me,
I just got away from death itself
I better go and do something else.

2003

A Robin's Christmas: Aidan Mitchell
Art: Sinéad Cummins

Snow

I fell from the sky
like a little white fly,
    I was left on the ground
       in a big white blanket.

      They built me up as a
      little white man
      they stuck in coal
      and put a hat on top.

As I glanced around
and watch them
throw my friends
I thought
how lucky I am.

eurochild 2003

Snow: Andrew O'Brien
Art: Emma Scott

Heartbroken

Miserable,
Awful,
Alone,
Useless,
Heartbroken,
Dull, never noticed, upset,
Unhappy, devastated,
But then it happened
I had a friend.
And it would never...
END.

Heartbroken: Keylan Fawsitt

2003 eurochild

(26)

Feelings

Feelings are some-
times happy or
sad,
feelings hurt.
Feelings can be
happy too.
My Granddad
died.
I felt devastated.
I thought it was a
nightmare.
I felt awful.
My heart was
paining me. But I know he is
happy and he watches me
every day. And if he is happy
I am happy too.

eurochild
2003

Feelings: Joanne Claxton
Art: Clare O'Rourke

The Silent Raider

Silent searching,
By the creature,
That you should never interfere with.
Silent swooping,
To catch its prey,
It's the owner of the night,
It's the Barn Owl.
It's taking its prey by surprise,
There he goes,
He's got his prize!

2003

The Silent Raider: Matthew Bruce Wallace

Frieden (Peace)

Nur ein Land, von tausend Ländern,
nur ein Tag, von Millionen Tagen,
nur eine Welt, von tausend Welten,
nur eine Galaxie, von tausend Galaxien,
nur ein Traum, den alle Träumen -
Frieden!

Trostlos

In mir, ist das Feuer ausgegangen,
alles erloschen, still sitze ich hier,
Regen, dunkler Himmel, keine Chance,
Hoffnung gibt es nun nicht mehr,
Es ist ausgegangen,
der Stern leuchtet nicht mehr in mir,
weg, erloschen, es ist trostlos,
seit du nicht mehr bei mir bist.

2003

Frieden: Frederike Buchta
Trostlos: Frederike Buchta

Das „Possierliche" Tierchen

Ich sehe eine Schuppe,
'ne Schuppe von 'nem Tier.
Das Tier ist klein und runzlig,
an Beinen hat es vier.

Arme hat's gleich sechse,
Augen dreieinhalb,
die Nase wie ein Nashorn,
die Hörner wie ein Kalb.

Der Schwanz besteht aus Flossen,
schön aneinand' gereiht.
Der Bauch ist eine Schuppe,
das Hirn nicht sehr gescheit.

Was ist es wohl für'n Tierchen,
so klein, so schön, so so?
Ach ist es nicht possierlich,
so süß, so leicht und froh?!

2003

Das „Possierliche" Tierchen: Thomas Faelligen & Vladimir Volinschi

Heaven

Is where the angels sing and
when Heaven opens up you can see
a golden staircase with a deep
red carpet leading up
to the white fluffy clouds and
your guardian angel singing louder
than the other angels. You
come up with a smile on your face,
for it is the end of your life.

My Sister's Gone

My Sister is gone
She's gone to New York.
She better come back with something for me.
She's finally gone but what shall I do.
I'll play with my teddies, watch some TV,
But she better come back with something for me.

2003 eurochild

Heaven: Lucy Arkley
My Sister's Gone: Eibhlin McDonagh

My School

School, school we are back to school.
Books on the table. Bag on the floor.
Work being done, tummy rumbling, lunch near.
Teacher comes, work gets done, bell rings.
Children running down the stairs into the yard,
children screaming, shouting. Whistle blows.
Children stop, line up and walk in, sit down,
have a drink, back to work, so little time until hometime.
Five minutes, put homework in diary, pack up go home.
Bye Bye.
Got to
go. See
you later.

The Night

The night has come,
The stars are out,
Time to go to bed,
Just love your house
It'll keep you warm
And not the garden shed.

2003 *eurochild*

My School: Megan Hobbs
The Night: Stacey Walsh
Art: Amy Nagle

A Robin in Our Holly Tree

There is a little robin in our Holly tree,
he sits there all evening, as happy as can be.
Then he sees a worm and has him for his tea.
And then goes to sleep as happy as can be.

2003 eurochild

A Robin in Our Holly Tree: Lauren McDonald
Art: Sarah Ryan

Buying a Book

I walk into a bookshop to get a book
I go to the children's section
I'm not interested in Bertie Aherne's last election
I see books about witches and wizards
Dinosaurs and lizards
Horror stories
Gruesome glories
Cookbooks
How to Look books
Books with fancy covers
That make children wail to mothers
Stories about brave knights in armour
Books about a selfish farmer
A book about a scarecrow that can talk
And finally a book about how to make children walk

My Dad comes over it's time to go
I can't make up my mind
There's nothing good I can find
Then I pick up a book with a nice look
And it turned out to be stupid.

Buying a Book: Eimear O'Sullivan

2003 eurochild

Is Santa Real

I

Is Santa real?
Do you know?
Because I would really like to know.

II

Is Santa real?
Coming down our chimney
Putting toys under our tree.
All the children in the world and me.

III

Is Santa real?
Delivering toys in the sleigh
All to open on Christmas Day.

IV

Is Santa real?
I would just like to know
Someone has to really know.

eurochild
2003

Is Santa Real: Emma Lovell

The Commanding Ball

One day I saw a ball
But it was stuck to the wall
I went over to get it
But first I had to sit

So I sat there
With my itchy hair
And waited and waited
But I never moved

A Poem

I went to Rome to write a poem
So I wrote the poem and came home

2003 eurochild

The Commanding Ball: Ronan Murphy
A Poem: Séan Lucey
Art: Adrienne McManus

Everyone Is Special

Everyone is special.
Everyone is good at something.
Nobody is bad at everything.
Everyone is special.
Everyone is good at something
Like swimming or climbing or baking or singing.
Everyone is special.

Springtime

In spring the flowers grow,
out and play you can go.
Daffodils, tulips everywhere,
lighter jumpers you can wear.
Sometimes in spring it is very hot,
but you will know if it is or not,
so remember to wear the right clothes
'cos you never know how the weather goes.

Everyone Is Special: Alice Coleman
Springtime: Clodagh Duggan

Natal é tempo de paz

Natal é tempo de paz.
Natal é tempo de harmonia.
Natal é tempo de amor.
Natal é tempo de alegria.
No Natal Nasceu Jesus.
Numa gruta em Bélem
Tão escura e tão fria
Que Maria sua mãe
Embrulhou-o em panos e faixas
E na manjedoura o deitou.
Uma vaquinha aqueceu-o
Um burrinho ajudou.
E o menino quentinho,adormeceu
Ao seu lado José e Maria
Cheios de amor, carhinho e alegria
Contemplo vom Jesus que dormia.

2003 eurochild

Natal é tempo de paz: 3/4 Class

A Amizade

A Amizade é uma paz importante
Ao cimo do Universo.
Amigos verdadeiros são uma paz feliz
Amigos falsos são uma paz infeliz
O sol é amarelo, a lua é azul
Não importa a cor, sim a amizade
Despeço-me deste poema
Com muita, muita amizade.

A Amizade: Cristiana Ferreira

Bangor My Home

I live in a place called Bangor
It lies beneath a hill
The river runs through it
Never, a moment still

The lake in all it's glory
Sees anglers from afar
The finest fish in Erris
Are lamented in 'West End Bar'.

Pairc an Tubair is my home place
Where my friends and I play
Our school withln walking distance
Where we sit and learn each day.

2003 eurochild

Bangor My Home: Kelly Geraghty
Art: Ann Eordanishvili

An Nollaig

Brat sneachta ar an talamh
Is Páistí ina luí,
Ag fanacht do Dhaidi na Nollag
Le gliondar 'nár gcroi'!

My Pets

My pets are very funny
but still are pretty annoying
and this is what goes on every day.
My mouse eats my cheese.
My cat eats my mouse.
My dog eats my cat.
My pig eats my dog.
My cow eats my pig.
And my cow still lives
since that very day.
But still I love them
all the same.

2003

An Nollaig: Colleen Ní Cheilleachair
My Pets: Jerri Ní Chróinín
Art: Cecile Autruffe

My Silly Family

My Mom is very silly.
She makes nice dinners.
Sometimes she makes disgusting dinners
with onions which I hate.
My Dad is very silly.
One day he fell over a banana
and he fell down the stairs.
He nearly broke his back
but he's o.k.
My sisters are very silly.
They put too much make-up on
and look very silly.
My brother is normal like me.
I like him very much.

2003 eurochild

My Silly Family: Niamh Ní Chonchúir

The Dog

There once was a dog,
Who ate a frog,
He had one good leap,
To land at a sheep,
He ate him as well,
He was banished to Hell,
He jumped to Japan,
To see Ireland v Iran
While eating a bun,
Ireland won,
The crowd was
not happy,
They threw a
used nappy,
It landed on
his head,
He woke up
in bed,
He coughed up some mutton,
It hit a button,
He blasted off
to space,
He was out of this race,
"What an adventure"; said he.

2003 *eurochild*

The Dog: Lee Sloan
Art: Rachel Maher

Special Olympics

This year in Ireland a great event will run,
Special people from all over the world will come.

There will be running, cycling, and swimming too,
Canoeing, horse riding and loads of other
Sports for the athletes to do.

If you can help in any way,
Maybe you have a place
For the athletes to stay.

It's coming to Ireland
It's lots of fun,
Check it out at a location near you,
Because there's fun for
EVERYONE!

Special Olympics: Alison Peate

Fleur tu as Perdu Toutes tes Couleurs

Fleur tu as perdu ton rouge flamboyant
Et ton jaune foudroyant

Fleur tu as ton bleu éclaircissant
Et ton gris d'orage.

Fleur tu as perdu ton violet resplendissant
Et ton orange pulsant

Fleur tu as perdu ton vert de printemps
Et ton rose endormant.

Fleur tu as perdu toutes tes couleurs

eurochild
2003

Fleur tu as Perdu Toutes tes Couleurs: Manuel Marolleau
Art: Ketevan Saradgishvili

Grandir

Franchir l'obstacle qui
Permet de grandir, de s'épanouir.

Grandir c'est aussi la malveillance
Et la désobéissance.

Partir, s'enfuir, vouloir mourir
Et tous ces pleurs et tous ces rires.

Mais je ne suis qu'un enfant
Un enfant qui court toujours dans les prés
Cherchant l'amour et la vérité.

2003 eurochild

Grandir: Charlotte Olivier

Les Bonnes Pâtisseries

Quand on pétrit le pain
On revient un beau matin
Avec une grosse pelle à la main
On cuit le pain tendre et moelleux
On en donnera à tous ceux
Qui nous aurons aidés comme des dieux

Après on prépare le
gâteau au chocolat
On prend un grand plat
On le prépare et hop va
Va dans le four et cuit
Le gâteau est réussi, il luit.
Comme cela est joli.

Les Bonnes Pâtisseries: Lucie Bodiguel
Art: Mick Byrne

Le Terrier

Le terrier
est bouché

Les fermiers
l'ont enfumé

Avec du châtaignier
et du noisetier

Le bois brulé
fait de la fumée

Les entrées
sont bouchées

Avec des rochers
craquelés

Pauvre chimpanzé
qui ne peut plus respirer

Mais il va creuser
il est sauvé
le chimpanzé

Le Terrier: Anne-Sophie Barbe

2003 eurochild

Mes voyages

J'aime voyager que ce soit en hiver ou en été,
De voir, de nouvelles faces du monde,
Pour découvrir le mystère, que la terre est ronde,
Maintenant je vais vous raconter ma vie,
Cette vie pleine de rimes belles
Alors voilà:

Bientôt j'irai en Espagne
Et ensuite à la campagne,
J'irai en plein air
Vers le bord de la mer,
J'irai en Russie
Ou visiter le mississipi,
Hier j'ai traversé la frontière
Au passage j'ai bu une bière.

Aujourd'hui j'ai fait des rimes
Car j'étais en Argentine,
Et voilà c'est fini,
Je vous ai montré toutes
sortes de pays infinis,
Au revoir mes amis.

Mes voyages: Yann Couchman et David Sherpa
Art: Vaclav Vlasak

Portugal

Porte bonheur, envoie nous un rayon unique de ta chaleur.
Ô paysage lointain
Retour en France nous ferait du chagin.
Toi Portugal, ouvre nous ton coeur.
Un village volé serait la pire chose à imaginer.
Grandeur sans décadence tout va de la seconde à l'heure.
Allô, coucher du soleil dis nous quand tu te réveilles.
La fin de ce poème, est faite pour te dire que l'on t'aime.

L'arc en Ciel

Pourquoi y a t-il des couleurs dans le ciel?
On est allé en avion dans les nuages
Pour dessiner au-dessus de nous?
Non! Non! Non! Et Non!
C'est peut être le soleil
Qui a des crayons feutres?
Non! Non! Non! Et Non!
C'est peut-être un projecteur
Qui envoie des couleurs?
Non! Non! Non! Et Non!
C'est tout simplement
L'ensemble du soleil et la pluie.

2003 eurochild

Portugal: Matthias Yohann
L'arc en Ciel: Natacha Ledue

A Amizade

Ainda, linda como o mar!
A Amizade à superficie.
Dois ou três amigos a nadar!
  Tão bonita esta palavra.
  "Amizade"!
      Não é?
        Ainda é importante para
          todos,
          Para ti, para mim,
          Como sabes um amigo
          Para confiar!
        Sem a Amizade não o poderias ter
Vais crescer, quando adulto fores
Olhares para este poema
Vai dizer: Amizade, lindo.

2003 eurochild

A Amizade: Vanessa Marto
Art: Séan Lucey

Behind Bars!

I am a simple elephant,
As you can see,
And I am here to tell you,
'Bout the people who stare at me.

They come in all shapes,
And sizes and lengths,
Some have square faces,
Or faces shaped like tents.

I like people, who look at me,
Who smile and say I'm cute,
But I hate people, who look at me,
And laugh with a hoot.

So next time remember,
I have feelings too,
So go and laugh at someone else,
Who lives in this zoo.

2003 eurochild

Behind Bars!: Stephanie Ryng

Crocodile Killer

One day in a pond.
I heard a sound.
It went bang, bang.
I ran along till I saw a van.
I saw a big man.
He was holding a gun.
Trying to kill a big crocodile.
I said "Hey man, don't shoot that crocodile
and turn him into a handbag."
The end.

Crocodile Killer: Tomás Walsh

My Pet

I have a pet called Ben.
I always dance with him.
He always follows me to the shed.
He always sniffs my toes.

My Bird

My favourite pet's name is Lucky
He sings all day and night.
His feathers are a bright yellow.
I love him with all my might.

We keep him in a cage.
I know it is not right.
Freedom would be better,
but alas he wouldn't last a night.

2003 eurochild

My Pet: Chloe Barrett
My Bird: Cíarraí O'Sullívan
Art: Rogan Quigley

The Prayer of a Dog

Dear God,
Please give me a comfortable kennel
And give me a kind master
Since they call me man's best friend
Give me the option to choose my master
Bless all dogs and all creatures that bark.

My Teacher is a Witch

My teacher is a witch.
She has a bad disguise.
She has a broom at the end of the class.
When we are in class she wears a scarf
To block out the wart on her neck.
What can I say?
My teacher is a witch.

2003 eurochild

The Prayer of a Dog: Sam Bartolo
My Teacher is a Witch: Caoimhe O'Donoghue
Art: Charlie Clarke

Le Caïman

Le caïman
Aux grandes dents
Attend.

Il attend
Dame Serpent,
Impatient
Il attend
Pendant un an
Dans le vent.

Il attend
Pendant un an
Sous les glands

Le caïman
Est mécontent
Car Dame Serpent
Est en Iran
Et elle attend un autre caïman.

2003

Le Caïman: Anne-Sophie Barbe

La Fin de l'Hiver

La glace en hiver
envahit mon corps de froid
la tristesse m'emporte

Sous les arbres embrumés
j'entend l'herbe gelée
crisser sous mes pieds.

Voir les fleurs s'ouvrir
je suis plein de joie au printemps,
quand je suis dans le bois.

Pluie et Neige Tombent

Pluie et neige tombent
quand grondement me répond
j'ai la joie en moi.

2003 eurochild

La Fin de l'Hiver: Sébastien
Pluie et Neige Tombent: Nahida

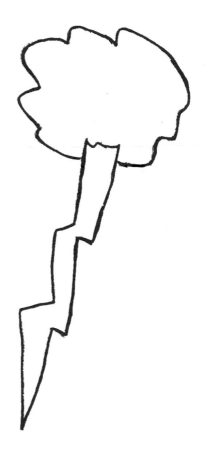

En Plein Hiver

En plein hiver,
Tombent les feuilles
Je suis très triste.

Le Tonnerre Grogne

Le tonnerre grogne,
Les sapins tremblent derrière moi
Les frissons montent dans le dos.

2003 eurochild

En Plein Hiver: Alexandre LM
Le Tonnerre Grogne: Alexandre G
Art: Alan O'Reagan

Comment Naissent les Bébés

D'abord, il faut un lit à deux places
Ensuite, il faut un homme et une femme.
Après, je jette un voile.
Pour ne pas vous influencer!
On fait des bébés comme ça.
On achète une grenouille femelle
Et une grenouille mâle.
Ils font des têtards.
Ce qui est le spermatozoïde.
Pour l'ovule c'est une autre histoire!
On achète un pigeon mâle
Et un pigeon femelle.
Ils font des oeufs.
Ce qui forme l'ovule.
Ensuite, vous prenez
un grand récipient
Vous y mettez le
spermatozoïde et l'ovule
Et vous mélangez!
Vous l'avalez!
Cela a drôle de goût!
Et neuf mois plus tard
Ouin ! Ouin ! Ouin !

eurochild
2003

Comment Naissent les Bébés: Titouan Nogue
Art: Diogo Santana

Mon Amie s'Appelle Emilie

Mon amie s'appelle Emilie
Elle aime plein de choses
Comme les chats et les roses
C'est ma meilleure amie
J'espère que c'est pour la vie
Quand elle sourit
Je la trouve très jolie
Quand elle danse
Elle me fait penser à la France
Elle habite à Cork
Et elle adore les orques.

La Musique

Elle trotte dans ma tête
petite bête
au rythme du bango
c'est très rigolo

2003 eurochild

Mon amie s'appelle Emilie: Claudia Sheridan
La musique: Louise Catinet

A Flower's Life

I am a flower so
colourful and bright.
To look my best I need
the sunlight.
I love the rain
it takes away all the pain.
Then the sun comes out
and dries me up again.

When autumn comes
my head gets low.
The wind starts to blow.
I am a petal
steaming in the kettle,
fallen in the window
and now I have to go.

eurochild
2003

A Flower's Life: John McCarthy
Art: Samantha Mueri

DUSKUNTA

eskusta pyörii tiellä,
ikka sitä ei kaivata siellä.
okoomus korjaa luusi!" Tarja heille huusi.
uki suusi!" Kokoomus takas huusi.
asemmistoliitto
n täysin finiitto
usi hallitus on tehtävä,
rvitaan idea lentävä,
 onnistu punamulta
ten sitä ei vaadita sulta.
uvi-Anne Siimes
ikkuu vasemmiston siives.
ätteenmäki,
n maha sillä kuin suuri mäki,
 puhuukin kuin vanha käki.

Paavo pyysi: "Anna mulle pulla, niin olo
hyvä on mulla
tai nenä murtunut on sulla."
Esko Aho
taas on latvastansa laho,
ei työreformia kukaan taho.
Kanervan Ilkka,
heittäkää sille ivallinen pikka.
Eduskunta,
sen vihamiehenä on luottokunta.
On kaikki varat käytetty,
ja budjetti menoilla täytetty,
ja oppositioelle ei sitä ole näytetty
Siis täs oli Suomen parlamentti,
on niillä aika kova temperamentti

2003

Eduskunta: Mikko Kivistö

Je ne sais pas Faire de Bêtises

Je ne sais pas faire de bêtises,
Mais il faut que je vous dise:
Mettre la mise
Sur une banquise
Avec des cerises de Venise
Est-ce une gourmandise
Ou une bêtise?

La Classe de Corinne

On passe aux Maths
et vous écrivez la date.
Les additions
sont mieux que les récréations.
Les cervelles sont parallèles.
Les français sont des dictées.
Les dictionnaires sont imaginaires.
La classe de Corinne est la plus coquine.

eurochild
2003

Je ne sais pas Faire de Bêtises: Mathias Lassfolk
La Classe de Corinne: Rebekka Hanslian

Le Petit Chat Gourmand

Le petit chat gourmand
a vu un gâteau
sur le buffet
qui ressemblait
a un château.
"Ce gâteau est encore chaud,
je vais le manger!"
se dit le chaton
"Mmm, que c'est bon,
mais maintenant je suis trop gros!"

2003 eurochild

Le Petit Chat Gourmand: Julia Ohela
Art: John O'Mahony

My First Day

My pencils are dirty,
my face is very grey
it sure feels weird,
cause it's my first day.

I need a pair of shoes,
I need my uniform today.
I need them now,
cause it's my first day.

I don't know what to talk about,
I don't know what to say
I wonder what my teacher is like
but I hope she is funny today.

I like the summer holidays,
but I hate this time of year
when we have to go back to school
it's really a pain in the ear.

2003 eurochild

My First Day: Stephen Ahern

Dans Mon Jardin

Dans mon jardin
Ce matin
Sous un rayon
J'ai vu un papillon
C' est merveilleux
Et fabuleux!
Mais il est parti ce soir
Alors au revoir!

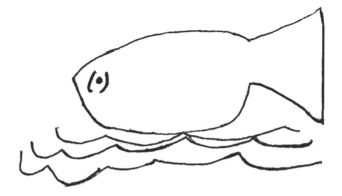

Le Poisson Ronchon

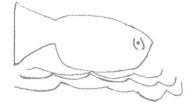

Un poisson ronchon
Faisait des bulles dans sa maison
Il aimait bien jouer au ballon
Mais quand il s'allongeait dessus
Pfuitt, il se retrouvait tout nu!
Il décide de manger un bonbon
L'avale et hop! meurt d'inattention...
Fin du poisson ronchon!

2003 eurochild

Dans Mon Jardin: Estelle Nakul
Le Poisson Ronchon: Christabel Haberlin
Art: Jennifer Hurley

Midnight Trout

On that night,
the hiss of snakes,
fire cracking by the lake.

I was fishing for a trout,
and I caught it from her mouth.
It started splashing in the lake,
when I caught it from the place.

It was time to go home
      because midnight was nearly gone,
         I ran towards my home,
            With the trout and fishing rod.

On my way, birds whistling, I heard
from the swishing trees,
and the shadows of the leaves,
made me run as fast as thieves.

I found myself behind the door,
of our little cottage home.
With a loud bang on the door,
I went in, and heard the sound;
of my father's roaring grump.
On the table I put the trout,
to go sleeping, for this night.

Midnight Trout: Charlot Borg
Art: Jason McSweeney

2003 eurochild

Tuvassa

Nurkassa kehräsi rukki
Katossa käveli lukki
Mikko tuli koulusta
Opettajat tulivat Oulusta
Käkikello kukkui
Tuvassa vauva nukkui

Kantele

Ullakolla kantele soi
Tonttu sen mulle toi
Kantele sateenkaaren väreihin pukeutunut on
Ilalla se varmaan riisunut ne jo on

Tuvassa: Matti Rahnasto
Kantele: Rebekka Hanslian

68

EL BÚHO

El búho marrón
Duerme de día
Y vigila de noche.
Por el bosque vagaba
Mientras hacía
Uh, uh, uh, uh.

El búho se reía
Y decía tonterías
Sobre la sequía.

Pero lo que él no sabía
Es que los demás búhos
A él le tenían...
¡ mucha manía !

2003

El Búho: Verónica Moya
Art: Sarah Casey

CADA DÍA

El sol brilla y brilla
Un lucero de calma
Y se mete cuando
Nos vamos a la cama.

Al amanecer
Vuelve a asomar
Por medio mundo
Y la otra mitad.

Esperando su llegada
Sin avisar.
Oh, oh, ya llega el sol
Y nos ciega entero
Con su gran resplandor.

ESOS ZAPATOS

Mis zapatos
Yo me los ato
Con los cordones
De colores.

Me gustan
Porque me los compró
Mi madre
Cuando fuimos
De vacaciones.

Mis zapatos
Siempre a tono
Con muchos hatos
Y mis cordones
De todos los colores.

Cadadía: Miriam López de la Franca
Esos Zapatos: Miriam López de la Franca

LA FRESA

La fresa es una fruta
Jugosa por dentro
Y que tiene una semillita
Allá por el centro.

Con ella se hacen batidos
Y también se dan chillidos
Cuando ya no quedan
En nuestro frigo.

MELÓN

Melón, melón
Por dentro sabor
Y por fuera su color.

Melón de verano
Melón, melón
Que te como yo

2003

La Fresa: Miriam López de la Franca
Melón: Ana Romero del Hombrebueno

De vacaciones no estoy
Más quisiera yo estar.
Contigo a tu lado
Qué bonito es cantar.

Caballos tenías.
Todavía tendrás.
Me dabas la vida
Con ese allí estar.

De noche
Iluminabas las calles de allá
Así con linternas
No teníamos que andar.

La gente con perros.
La gente con gatos.
La gente con ranas
En sus caravanas.

Y aquella amiga
Llamada Carolina
¡Qué pesadita!
¡Qué pesadita!

2003

Palacio de Garaña: María del Mar Simal
Art: Jessica Gayeova

Oíche Shamhna

Chonaic mé chailleach ghránna,
Ag eitilt tríd an spéir,
Hatá dubh ar a cheann,
Agus í ag ithe suipéir.

Thosaigh an ghealach ag gáire,
Agus sheas an chat ar a lapa,
"Fóir orm, Fóir orm" arsa an chat,
Táimíd ag dul róthapa.

An t-Earrach

Bláthanna ag Fás sa gháirdin.
Paistí ag súgradh faoin spéir,
Éin ag canadh sa chrainn,
Agus madra ag tafann ar an bhféar.

Lacha ag snámh sa loch.
Coíníní ag rith faoin gcrann
Uain ag léim agus ag rince
Agus gráinneog mhór ann.

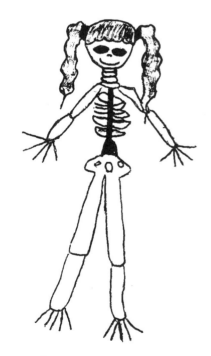

2003 eurochild

Oíche Shamhna: Sarah Kavanagh
An t-Earrach: Heather Kearney and Alysha Hoare
Art: Lucy Arkely

värit

Punainen on rakkauden
Keltainen on kiltteyden
Sininen on uskollisuuden
Oranssi on vain yksin

vuodenajat

Kun on talvi pitää olla pääsä pipo,
älä tankoa lipo
koska silloin kiinni jää kieli

Kun on kësa
linnuilla on pesä.
Silloin olen isällä
kun on kuuma sisällä

Kun on syksy
Puut heiluttaa lehdet
Silloin keinuja keinuttaa saa.

2003 eurochild

värit: Kristina Väyrynen
vuodenajat: My Paasivaara

Poika Oulussa

Oli poika joka asui oulussa
ja se kävi kansakoulussa.
Mutta ei millään pahalla
sen isä ajaa töihin Ladalla.
Kaikki häntä siitä pilkkaa,
mutta silloin he nenästänsä kaivavat veritilkkaa,
sillä se poika on hyvin vahva
sen sormissa murtuu jopa ovenkahva.
Kun loppui koulu ja tuli joulu
se sai lahjaksi pelkkiä kukkia ja vähän villasukkia
Sukat se heiti pois ja pukille huus että
"parempi ilman näitä ois!"
Silloin sen äiti suuttui
ja sen pojan käytös täysin muuttui.
Eikä se enää haittaa että
isä kaasutti Ladallaan,
koska nyt se makaa kaatopaikalla mahallaan.
On isällä uusi sitikka
sen päälle ei kaki edes itikka.

2003 eurochild

Poika Oulussa: Olavi Lyyra

Soccer

I like the game of soccer.
I play it every day.
My favourite team is Man U.
And I hope on top they'll stay.
My favourite player is Keano
who is always in the news,
for when he scores the winning
goal or when he blows a fine!
There is a duck called Beckham
with a lovely wife called Posh.
He drives a sleek Mercedes
"That guy has loads of dosh".
O'Shea is the latest player to
make it on the team.
I'd like to meet him one day
but for now it's just a dream.

2003 eurochild

Soccer: Ronan Cotter
Art: David Aherne

Ajatus

Talvella lumi peittää ruohon,
puut ja talojen katot.
Keväällä on lämpimämpää
ja lumet sulavat.
Kesällä pääsee uimaan, ja lomalle.
Syksyllä pitää panna takki päälle
koska alkaa tulla kylmempää.
Puiden lehdet alkavat tippua.

Etsin Ja Löysin

Sisältä läheltä etsin
Ulkoa kaukaa löysin
Sieltä sen kotiin yritin viedä
Mutta kadulle jäipan se vielä
Kun hypin se käveli
Kun lauloin se rääkyi
Kun komensin se puhui
Siis en sille voinut mitään
Kotiin palasin hyppien
Sepä käveli rääkyen

eurochild
2003

Ajatus: Marcos Ryhänen
Etsin ja löysin: Rossitsa Kauppinen

Is it a Beautiful World?

What a beautiful world
A little world
I wish it was so sure
Because of wars
It isn't true.
Bombs are falling everywhere
Starvation in poor countries
Crying, dying everyday
Heartaches everywhere.
Let's pray for our world
To be beautiful and peaceful
I pray that all the people
See sunshine again.

2003 eurochild

Is it a Beautiful World?: Jonathan Carter
Art: Katie O'Reilly

Devil

Bad tempered devil
Red-hot devil from hot Hell
Here he comes for me

Spring

At the start of Spring,
I hear the birds sing,
A sweet little song,
As they fly along,
I see bluebells rise,
Out the corner of my eyes,
Daffodils are coming,
And the bees are humming,
Spring is my favourite season,
And it's plain to see my reason!!!

2003 eurochild

Devil: Jeffrey London
Spring: Paula Maher
Art: Harry Porter

Dawn at Buschetto Gardens

Look all around you
And enjoy
The beauty of nature
Which fills up with you

Birds flying
From tree to tree
Singing as merrily
As can be

Singing filtering
Through the trees
Forming amazing patterns
With the breeze

Myriads of flowers
Like a carpet spread
Fantastic colours
Forming a bed

Butterflies flying
Here and there
The smell of oranges
Is everywhere

Hear the sounds
Feel the breeze
Relax and admire
Feel at ease

Thanks God everything
That you see
Feels the power of goodness
Of God Almighty

2003 eurochild

Dawn at Buschetto Gardens: Mario Micallef

A Different World

I love to read any book,
Any book I can find,
After a while reading the book,
I enter a different world in my mind.

When reading a book you can forget,
Any problems you might have,
Relax! Hear of the troubles,
And adventures of people you have never met.

Books are great for all,
Full of fantasy dreams and fun,
So go on - pick up a book,
Because with books you're never done,

And remember -
Never judge a book by it's cover!

A Different World: Catrióna Beckles

The Princess' Rescue

There was once a princess at the top of a king's tower,
She couldn't get down, for she was up there for hours.
The King grounded her for being so bold,
But what she had done was not to be told.
Then along came the handsome prince on his steed,
who knocked on the door - no reply he received.
So around went the prince to the back of the tower,
He awaited his princess to give her a flower.
She appeared at the window and gave a big sigh,
For she had nothing to do but look up at the sky.
The prince fetched his rope and swung it up high,
The princess knew that her rescue was nigh.
She clenched on the rope and swung down in a flash,
They sat on the young steed and were off in a dash.
The beautiful princess wasn't sad anymore,
For she lived with the prince forever more.

2003 eurochild

The Princess' Rescue: Shauna Hogan
Art: Donna Condon

Stopping By a Beach

I feel the sun beaming
down on me.
I see the wave's crash
against the rocks.
I sense the breeze
blowing my hair.

The sand silky and soft.
The water cold and blue.
I know I'm at my favourite
place it's the beach which is my home too.

My Favourite Place

I stopped by the woods one day
And what I saw was not full of grey
The birds were singing to their friends
And I hoping this day never ends
The butterflies flying up and down
The flowers smiled and did not frown
The stoney path that will never end
And that's my favourite place, my friend.

eurochild
2003

Stopping By a Beach: Alice Donnelly
My Favourite Place: Eoin Kimmage
Art: Teona Kokhodze

The Storm

The wind was howling for miles around
The gate flung open without a sound
The trees went from side to side to side
Some branches broke, some branches died.

The dogs were barking,
The cats meowing
The foxes ran to their dens.
Their feet mucking up the ground.

No Shoes, Beautiful Toes

I've got style
I've got groove
I've got clothes
But I've no shoes

So when I go out on the street
I see people staring at my feet
But my toenails are the most pretty sight,
I've seen in all my life

The Storm: Sarah McNally
No Shoes, Beautiful Toes: SallyAnn Downes
Art: Teona Kokhodze

2003  eurochild

Fox

Hunting, Searching
Against the green fields, hills and flowers
He finds a mouse
And starts to carry it home.
He sniffs,
A smell, a strange smell,
Mingled with the country air.
A noise
Horns, blowing loud, an unusual sound.
A hunt,
Hounds, horses and men
Trampling the sweet, long, grass
He runs
A fast, red, streak across the hills.
A river

A deep, wide river
Hope for him
He swims across
The hounds lose track.
Safety
The fox slows down,
Catches his breath
Bright eyed, bushy tailed, red fur
A wonder to behold.
The earth
A safe, quiet, place
With cubs, warmth, and a spot to shelter
He lies down, goes to sleep.
The cunning, sly fox outsmarts the human
Once again.

eurochild
2003

Fox: Marianne Kennedy

Moon

Sparkling, twinkling, silver moon
Up so high, a silver balloon.
Gently lighting up the sky
While Mother sings a lullaby.

2003 *eurochild*

Moon: Aileen O'Mahony
Art: Andrea Delicata

The Storm

The winds were howling for miles around
The leaves blowing from all around
The rain was dancing on the ground
Then there was a great big sound of thunder
A flash of lightning lit the sky it was so
frightening I did start to cry

Standing Still

Standing by only takes a minute
To escape from reality
To look at a scene and
Time will stand still
And you will forget yourself
You will be swept up with the
Beauty and
Be lost with the wonder
But all too soon reality
Catches up with you

2003 eurochild

The Storm: Mark Moore
Standing Still: Aoife Byrne
Art: Sean Tracy

Stopping by Mountains

When we went on holidays
in our new car,
I loved to look at the scenery,
so we travelled on quite far.
In the distance I can see
the mountains so beautiful,
this is the picture for me.
I said to my dad will you
please stop here.
So I reached for my camera
to get a good shot,
the beautiful sight I have never forgot!!

Christmas

When you put up a Christmas Tree,
When you're a busy little bee,
Then help out your mam,
Eating turkey and ham.
A snowman in a field of white,
A bright star in the night.

2003

Stopping by Mountains: James Halligan
Christmas: Niamh Tully

Tänään

Kun mä tänään herään,
se tekee kyllä terää.
Mä pesen ensin naaman
ja katson samall' draaman.
Mä harjaan nopee hampaat
ja hoidan sitten lampaat.
Kun mä kouluun lähden,
niin ikkunast' nään tähden.
Kun ehdin kouluun,
mä myös sinne ajoissa tuun.
Koulussa kun saa olla,
niin Mathias opettaa mitä on nolla.
Kun mä kotona jälleen oon,
ja opettelin sävelen do.
Ja menen nukkumaan
sekä kaakaota saan.

Tänään: Kristian Tuurna

Oíche Shamhna

Oíche shamna a bhí ann,
Cheannaigh Mamaí cnónna.
Thosaigh mé ag súgradh sa chrann,
Agus tháinig mo chara Fíona.

Rinneamar mascanna gránna,
Bhí Mamaí ag ullmhú an súipeir.
Chonaic na paistí Chailleach Ghránna,
Ag eitilt go hard sa spéir.

Rabbits

Little furry rabbits
In the field at play
Just a quiet footstep
They all run away.

Down into their burrows
There they go to hide
Now they're safe together
Cuddled side by side.

2003 eurochild

Rabbits: Rebecca Dooley
Oíche Shamhna: Aimee Millar and Katie O'Donoghue
Art: Barbora Krizova

Na Duilleoga

Chonaic mé duilleoga,
Ag eitilt sa spéir.
Ag casadh, ag titim,
Anuas ar an bhféar.

Duilleoga dearg, donn,
Agus glas.
Chic me duilleoga
Le mo chós.

Go tobann, thosaigh an stoirm sa spéir.
Rith me abhaile go tapa,
Duilleoga ag damhsa
Duilleoga ag eitilt
Anuas, anuas ar mo hata.

2003 eurochild

Na Duilleoga: Grace O'Mahoney and Amy Kate Trevor

The Amazing General Bear

I know a super hero
His name is General Bear
He's six foot tall with a machine gun
And he is a teddy bear!

He fights evil doers
He punishes lords of crime
He locks them up in jail
And saves lives all the time.

He wears a long black cape
And smokes a little pipe
He has a posh English accent
And is a jolly type.

He fought the Radio-Active Owl
Who wrecked a nice fun fair
He has a secret identity
That he wouldn't even
Tell the Mayor.

2003 eurochild

The Amazing General Bear: Gerard Joseph Sexton

Art: Gerard Joseph Sexton

Mam! Mam!

"Mam, why do we have to clean our room?"
"Cause I told you to!"
"But Mam, I don't have to!"
"Oh yes you do,'cause your room is a mess."
"But..."
"No 'buts'. Now, clean your room!"
"But Mam, I don't want to."
"You have to."
"But..."
"The others can draw a picture."
"But..."
"Didn't I say no 'buts'?"
"I don't want to clean my room."
"Mam! Mam"
"Mam! Mam! MaaaaaAAAMMM!"
"Rebecca. You're punished."
"Mam!"
"That's because you were rude!"

Mam! Mam!: Rebecca Dooley

The Chaos

"Pack up the socks"
"Don't forget the books"
This is the chaos we
all live in. This happens
daily, in house-moving and
going to school. The stress,
the stress, of it all, can't
people stay, and relax and
sit back. Why do they have
to make that much stress.

My Spanish Cat

My cat came to Ireland on a plane
From a very sunny place called Spain.
My cat sits on the shelf in the sun
Which she considers so much fun.
I love my cat even though she's kind of fat.
She heaves herself to her food bowl,
and then leaves it terribly slow.
She goes to find the sun
thinks of Spain and lots of good fun.

The Chaos: Sebastian Stock
My Spanish Cat: Drew Emmer Wilkinson
Art: Mick Byrne

94

MI PUEBLO PERDIDO

Pueblo, pueblo perdido.
Miraré tu reloj desde mi balcón.

Y cuando me vaya
Me iré con mucho dolor.

Pero siempre estarás allí
En mi alrededor

Y seguiré mirándote
Desde mi balcón.

Pueblo, pueblo perdido
Recordaré el reflejo de tu reloj.

2003 eurochild

Mi Puelbo Perdido: Martin Serrano Aránzazu
Art: Ann Eordanishvili

PAN, PAN...

Pan, pan ¡ qué rico manjar
Cuando hay que mojar !
Con una sopa
Todos van, todos van.

¡ Ay ! Pan, pan
¡ qué rico manjar !
trigo, harina y huevo
mojar con el dedo.

¡ Ay, el rico pan con las
hadas
se hace nombrar !

RÍO SAGRADO

El río Sagrado era muy caudaloso
Y también dicen que era muy peligroso,
Pero los niños se mantenían muy silenciosos
Para poder escuchar cómo era de ruidoso.

2003 eurochild

Pan, Pan...: Ana Maria de la Rosa
Río Sagrado: Aránzazu Martin Serrano

Movement Of Life

The movement of life
The light of the burning sun
Sea like a sapphire

Rachel

An angel was sent from heaven above,
A special one that would bring much love.
God knew that this precious life would be short,
So he looked around for a tender heart.

The choice was made, the angel was sent,
In what seemed like a moment the angel went,
Leaving treasured memories
And a heart full of pain behind.

What seemed like an age, when only a year has gone past.
God's choice was right from the start
You're maybe gone from this world,
But not from our hearts.

eurochild
2003

Movement of Life: Séan Travers
Rachel: Aoife O'Leary
Art: Aileen Mc Auliffe

The Disappearance

Once there was a girl
And she was really sad,
She was never happy
She was never glad.

When she went to school
Everyone was cool,
And she always felt
Like a fool

One day she ran away from home
She was never seen again,
When the clock struck twelve that night
She stepped forward with no fear or fright.

She opened her arms like nothing was wrong
And then she realised she was gone.
Her parents would be crying.
They knew she would be found
Lying there on the ground.

2003

The Disappearance: Séan Travers

My Cat

My black cat
My black fluffy cat
My black fluffy small cat
My black fluffy small fat cat
My black fluffy small fat dirty cat
My black fluffy small fat dirty stinky cat
Wait, that's a dog!

The Boy Without any Toys

Once there was a boy
without any toys
he would like some
but he hadn't one
he felt quite sad
his mum was quite glad
that he was the boy
without any toys

2003 eurochild

My Cat: Katie O'Donovan
The Boy Without any Toys: Nicola Kerr
Art: Louise Welch

My Nana

I heard you're feeling a bit blue
So I picked a flower for you!
Me and my pony went into the field
To gather a bunch of flowers,
but to gather a bunch good enough for you
we knew would take hours and hours
So I picked one down by the lake
A beautiful crystal white
And I knew that when you saw it
you'd look at me with delight.
When I got there you asked me to come in
With a warm smile on your face
And Jack was in the hallway
looking for a chase
You cuddled me and said 'I love you'
So I cuddled you back and said
"I love you too!"

My Nana: Sarah Cotter

Poor Man

There was an old man, who lived in a shoe,
He was hungry, didn't know what to do,
Some gave him some broth, but he wanted stew,
He drank soup, and he bid them adieu.

This little poor old man, went a fishing,
For to catch a whale, but all he could get,
Was a black shoe, so he started crying,
He fell in the river, and went home wet.

He went to the cupboard to get a cake,
But when he went there, the cupboard was bare,
The man was hungry he wished he could bake,
To go and beg again, he wouldn't dare.

This little poor old man tattered and torn,
Went to bed and wishing he had never been born.

eurochild
2003

Poor Man: David Gauci

101

My Dream

My drem is to fly into the air
To waltz with the birds
To sing a prayer
To dive in the ocean
And give everyone a scare
My dream is to fly into the air

I know that my dreams
Will always be with me
As long as I live
They may not all come true
But I'll try very hard
In all that I do

2003 eurochild

My Dream: Katie O'Sullivan
Art: Courtney O'Sullivan

Two Dogs on a Lawn

Two dogs on a lawn
one begins to yawn
lie there sleeping
one eye peeping
Dad's new hat
must chew that!
Wake to eat
hope it's minced meat.
Back on the lawn
too tired to yawn
fast sleeping, no eyes peeping.
Let them be
they're familiar to me
because they're mine.

2003 eurochild

Two Dogs on a Lawn: Louise McKeown
Art: Niamh Brady

Hidden Danger

Sometimes I'm scared to walk,
Alone in my park,
When it gets dark,
I even jump if I hear dogs bark,
I cannot play outside with my fiends,
When it gets late,
Because it's not safe.

The sun may shine,
But there is still crime,
Some of the criminals don't do the time,
We must not forget,
That those people don't regret,
Making us fret,
Who's going to draw the line?
Because there is no need for crime.

2003 eurochild

Hidden Danger: Christina Walsh

Fish

Fish they live in the sea.
All colours and sizes.
They're a delight to see.
Swishing and swaying
On the seabed.
Yellows, greens, blues and reds.

My Dream Is...!

My dream is to be a popstar
Just like S Club Juniors.
They are so great
Just like my best mates.

If I were famous
I'd be a great star
And have lots of money
And drive a red sports car.

If I were famous
I'd have a handsome honey
And of course my handsome honey,
Would have lots of money.

104

2003 eurochild

Fish: Amy Wallace
My Dream Is...!: Sinead O'Brien
Art: Catrióna Beckles

Ice-Cream

At the start it's just one
Then it's two, three and four.
My mom and my dentist
Can't take it any more!

All the colours of the rainbow
It's like in a dream
And I love it so much
It's called ice-cream

Mom said that
I'm wasting money on it
And I'll probably
End up with a zit.

But in the end it does seem
That I'm absolutely in love with
ICE-CREAM!!!!

Ice-Cream: Sinead O'Leary

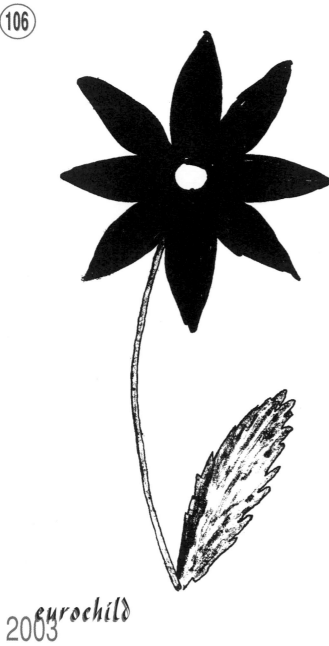

Síochán

Will there be war in 2003,
An mbeidh eitleáin ag scaoileadh,
Na Míllí buamaí.

Will my life change forever,
because of America and Iraq,
Leis an troid agus saighdiurí,
Cad a bheidh fágtha, ceapaim faic.

Let's wish for peace not war
no victims, no killings,
Guimís arís nach dtiocfaidh an
cógadh, agus beidh siocháin
ag gach duine.

2003 eurochild

Síochán: Angie O'Donnell
Art: Jessica Gayeova

My Mum

My Mum is the best in the whole wide west.
She loves me and I love her.
She brings us places.
Where we have never been.
She buys stuff for Halloween, Birthday, Christmas, Easter too.
So I decided to buy her a new pair of shoes.

Autumn

A is for autumn with leaves of gold.
U is for unbelieveably cold.
T is for trick or treating young and old
U is for singing songs as told
M is for me going in early at night
N is for nothing but rain in sight.

2003 eurochild

My Mum: Teri Cort Davis
Autumn: Emma Quirke

Special Olympics

People may be different,
But what matters is you know,
They don't need reminding,
Everywhere they go.

There's no need to whisper,
Or talk behind their backs,
In fact I think you're lucky,
If there's someone special in your
class.

Don't laugh at their mistakes,
Try to see what they achieve,
If you're saying stuff just to be
popular,
You're really just being mean.

Help them if they fall behind,
And in the end I'm sure,
That once you get to know them,
You'll have one friend more.

Don't do it out of pity,
They won't appreciate it,
Just hope the others will realise,
That themselves, They're not so
great.

That's why there are Olympics,
For special people in the world,
And An Post are the sponsors,
Haven't you heard?

They train really hard,
Golf, Basketball, Tennis too,
And spend a long time wishing,
For their dreams to come true.

eurochild
2003

Special Olympics: Paula Cashel

Elvis Spotted in Co. Mayo

I went up to Mayo the other day,
And you wouldn't believe what I
heard people say.
"I saw it myself, it's really true"
"The King is back, O whoopdedoo!"

I stood and stared as they screamed and screamed.
It wasn't possible, "I don't believe it!"
"Go up to the bog" a fat man said,
"You'll see him there", was on his head.

I went up the hill, to the bog by the river,
I heard a noise, it made me shiver,
Then from behind me I heard someone
singing an Elvis song,
I gave a big applause at the last gong,
Then upon my shoulder I felt a touch,
I turned to hear, "Thank you, thank you very much!"

2003

Elvis Spotted in Co. Mayo: Niamh Scanlon
Art: Seán Travers

The Moon

I am the moon, shining bright,
Every single wondrous night.
Never lonesome with
the twinkling stars,
my friends the planets,
especially Mars.

Gleaming and glowing
through the sun's shadow,
down on the cows,
scattered in the meadow.
The shimmering rivulets
of the silent lake,
Broken by the hoot of an
owl, now awake.

In the distant farmyard,
the cock crows,
time to disperse, everyone knows.
The sun appears behind a hill,
a little boy watches, atop his windowsill.

eurochild
2003

The Moon: Sarah Ryan
Art: Elaine Long

Poetry!

Some poets can express themselves in
wonderful, catchy, clever ways!
That depresses me because I want to be
able to express myself like that,
but the words come out all jumbled,
I had it perfect in my head
and even this poem came out wrong!

2003 eurochild

Poetry!: Niamh Collins

A Friend

A friend for life is a friend indeed
To hold your hand when you're in need
To stay with you no matter what
To keep you cool when it gets hot

A friend is someone there for you
To share in stuff you want to do
To guide you through the rough times
And help you make up silly old rhymes

A friend is brave, strong and mighty
And maybe a little flighty
Your friends will be for ever more
And true friendship is never a chore.

2003 eurochild

A Friend: Rebecca Morley
Art: Emily Holland

Eurochild

Teacher announces the *Eurochild* book,
And says "If anyone's interested please listen and look."
Enter a poem of your own that you like,
Put in more than one...different types.
The minute I heard this, I came alive,
Words and poems came into my head that I can't even describe.
Rhyming words like 'high' and 'pie',
Something that will catch their eye.
At last it's ready, it's about the actual book,
When I think about all the work it took.
Children around the world will hand in their poems,
Then all they can do is hope and pray,
To be walking into Tigh Filí,
On that one fine day.

Eurochild: Jennifer Barry

Homework

Homework,
We get too much,
The teachers think it's not enough,
I hate homework,
It's no fun
I've all sorts of exuses
As to why it's not done.
Homework,
Slaving away till it's nine or ten,
Then the teacher screams,
"It's too messy, do it again!"
Reading,
Writing,
Learning too,
I hate homework,
Do you?

eurochild
2003

Homework: Daire O' Sullivan
Art: Олимпия Симопулу

(115)

Limerick

There once was a boy from Cork,
Who used never eat with his fork,
His Mum and Dad,
Said he was very bad,
So then they just fed him with pork!!!

Bus, Bus

Bus, Bus
pepper, pepper
salt, salt
butter, butter
out, out
in and out.
Salad, salad, salad, salad,
flower, flower, flower, bower,
goo loo, goo loo, poo loo.
Ear, earwig, wait to peer.

2003 eurochild

Limerick: Janine Mohally
Bus, Bus: Lili MacMonagle

My Dream Land

Whenever I close my eyes and dream,
I think of a clean water stream,
There is a place in my head
Where no one ever goes to bed.

The moon at day and the sun at night
In my land there is no fight,
Everyone has a licence to fly
There are birds of paradise in the sky.

There is a little village up in the clouds
Where no one is ever noisy and no one is ever loud
There are butterflies and candy and lots of pretty flowers
If my wish did come true I would stay there for hours.

gyrochild
2003

My Dream Land: Katie O'Sullivan
Art: Khatia Dzimistarishvili

The Christmas Girl

So what if I'm alone as could be,
Why do people pass and look like that at me,
Who cares if I'm alone on Christmas Day,
My family has passed on but I'm here to stay,
Then suddenly a woman walks right up to me
"You poor thing, are you alone as alone could be"
She brought me home with her and wrapped me in a rug,
She gave me chocolate biscuits and milk in a mug,
She gave me socks and juicy gums,
She showed me her daughters and her sons,
She gave me shoes and proper clothes to wear,
Then she said "goodbye and take care",
But I'm still alone as alone could be,
Will I ever belong to a family.

2003 eurochild

Christmas Girl: Niamh Lynch

Special Olympics

The Olympics will start in 2003,
They're special you know, to you and to me!,
Contestants will come with pride in their hearts,
To finish the race having been at the start,
There's running and swimming and archery too,
They're having great fun with the things that they do,
So, I wish them good luck and to do very well!

2003 eurochild

Special Olympics: Lorna Curran

Friends

We've been through so very much
all throughout the years.
We've shared so much laughter
and there's also been some tears.
Friendship is a precious thing
to be cherished everyday.
Friendship is a special thing
never to be left go astray.

2003 eurochild

Friends: Emma Counihan
Art: Paul Martin

Mr Snowman

I

There is a snowman who is short and fat.
He lives in my garden and scares the cat.
He has three buttons right up his tummy
and as for his nose he has but a rose!

II

He has been there for a long time now.
Do I know why he's there?
Well no, I really don't.
I tried to get him to talk once
but no he just won't.

III

He is still not gone now
after what 5 days now
the sun is out and it's starting to glaze.
Goodbye Mr Snowman you must go now
but don't leave with tears
you could always take a bow!

Mr Snowman: Joanne O'Mahony
Art: Miriam Minihane

On Christmas Eve

I

On Christmas Eve
I like to fill
The crib full of creatures
Standing tall and still.

II

Mary and Joseph
and Jesus of course
all slept in Bethlehem
With the cow and the horse.

III

When the wise men came
And the shepherds as well
The great kings came
With a story to tell.

IV

They sat there all night
While the great kings told the story
And when they finally got to sleep
The sun dawned for it was morning.

On Christmas Eve: Vivienne Murphy

2003 eurochild

Goodbye Mum

You look at me with loving eyes
The fire gone out of your heart
Why did it have to be you Mum?
I need you.
I need you to hold my hand when I'm sick
To comfort me when I am sad
I wish you could comfort me now Mum
But you can't.
And I wish I wasn't losing you Mum
But I am.
What will it be like without you Mum?
I can't even imagine it
But I can't stop you going Mum.
And you're slowly slipping away
And when your gone Mum
Look down on me from Heaven
Please watch me growing up.
So Goodbye Mum
Forever.

2003 eurochild

Goodbye Mum: Laurie O'Keeffe

Under My Bed

Under my bed
It's dark and it's damp
It's really, really scary
For a dreadful monster
Comes out at night
And nibbles at my toes
One night I brought my flashlight
Into my double bed
And that night when it started
I saw my hamster Ted.

Under My Bed: Aimee O'Driscoll
Art: Sophie Bernard

Teacher! Teacher!

Teacher, teacher, I want to know
How long does it take for a orange to grow?
How high can a bird fly before it gets tired?
And why do hyenas laugh like they're wired?
Teacher, teacher just tell me this much!
Is there a cure for asking questions too much?

2003 eurochild

Teacher! Teacher!: Claire Allen
Art: Megan Hobbs

Old Fashioned Gran

I
My gran is so old fashioned,
For example my cousin would be wearing
A flowery dress
But Gran would call it
"A floral frock"

II
I mean nobody uses
The word "frock" anymore
And she is still converting her money
Back to shillings and crowns

III
But I suppose that's why
My Gran Peg Kelly
Is so special to me.

2003 eurochild

Old Fashioned Gran: Amy Ormond

Colours

Red is the colour of a
newly budded rose,
That sways in the breeze
and tickles your nose.

Yellow is the colour of
the bright dawning sun,
With daffodils' faces as
round as iced buns.

Pink is the colour of a
baby's chubby cheeks,
That blow up like balloons
whenever it speaks.

Blue is the colour of
the gleaming sky,
It's where you go up when
you have just died.

eurochild
2003

Colours: Aoife McDonald

Football

When I am playing football with my friends,
I hope to God it will never end.
I have so much fun kicking the ball,
That I never cry if I trip or fall.

I always laugh and have fun,
But then I think, there's a game to be won.
I kick the ball, the crowd gives a roar,
It glides through the post for the final score.

I've been playing football since primary school,
I have got the same coach and he's really cool.
Being a star is my dream,
I only hope I get on the team.

2003 eurochild

Football: Rhea Tummon
Art: David Cubbard

Wintertime

Wintertime is here again,
The hungry fox is in his den.
Ravenous birds look for food,
Not a time for playful mood.
Dreary nights bleak and dark,
For now no playtime in the park.
Snow is falling hip hip hooray!
And school is cancelled for the day.
Snowmen standing, snowball pelting,
Tell me quickly if it's melting.
Stormy winds on the way to schools,
Stepping into cold wet pools.
Through the winter some animals sleep
Until the Spring when up they leap.
The wintery conditions are such a bummer,
I'd much prefer a nice warm summer.

eurochild
2003

Wintertime: Alanah Cooney
Art: Ruth Zajacova

Why I Cannot Come to School Today!

Dear Teacher,
I cannot come to school today,
I broke my leg in an awkward way,
When I walk I feel dizzy and my
head is in a tizzy, when I talk,
The words don't come out right,
I really look an awful sight,
I have infection in my right and left ear
It's a wonder I can hear,
I received a punch that nearly caused amnesia
If I come to school I might disease ya!
I stuck a pencil in my eye
Oh no! I think I'm going to die!

Dear Tara,
Tara I think you're playing the fool,
You don't have to go school,
I'm sorry for what you have to say,
But today's a holiday!
As soon as I had read this letter,
I decided I felt much better!

Why I Cannot Come to School Today!: Tara Higgins

Snow

Today the snow came tumbling
In flakes as sweet as lace.
It danced and whirled, white and soft,
Like petals on my face.

Noel and I went running,
Scooping armfuls to make a snow-
man.
It was fun to watch him grow.

Now the sun is setting,
All pink across the white.
The snowman looks quite lonely
Standing in the fading light.

So I've come outside to talk to him.
I say "Now don't be so sad,
The sheep will keep you company"
And he smiles as if he's glad.

eurochild
2003

Snow: Aishling Hennessy
Art: Marie Hartmannova

I Saw a Little Angel...

I saw a little angel stand outside my door.
Her reflection shone upon the kitchen floor.

I wondered if I would scare her away, if I
invited her to come in and stay.

She looked pretty in her white linen dress,
all covered with lilies...and me in a mess.

I called for her to come in and play...
but she just smiled and faded away.

I still remember the feeling that day of seeing
an angel, so close and yet so far away.

2003 eurochild

I Saw an Angel: Rachel Stockes

The Accepting Land...Ireland

There could be a faint light at the end of the tunnel,
Please will you let us in?
We hope to hurry off the crowded ship,
Screaming and shouting, pushing and pulling,
They're turning us away again.

I see a hungry baby softly crying,
I feel sorry for the mother who quietly sighs,
When will this dreadful night be over?
When will the sun rise?
But they're not letting us in,
Looks like we'll be travelling all night.

It is three in the morning, this is our seventh stop tonight,
I see a patch of lush green fields,
There is a welcome sense in the clean fresh air,
Could this be it?
I think it is,
Everyone is relieved as we step off the ship
and onto the accepting land,
Ireland.

2003 eurochild

The Accepting Land...Ireland: Emma Cuddihy

Brothers

Bad
Rotten
Over tempered
Terrible
Horrible
Envious
Really mean
Sometimes nice!?

133

2003 *eurochild*

Brothers: Jessica Higgins
Art: Gillian Small

The Four Hillbillies

They flew to Africa
To climb Kilimanjaro
The four brave men
Pondered on this

There was no looking back
They had beaten Carrantoohill
One misplaced foot
And it was OVER

When they reached the top
It was nothing but smiles
They made the town proud
And will come back as HEROES

The Four Hillbillies: Gavin O'Driscoll

Banners in The Breeze

War has almost started
No one really knows what to do
The soldiers load up at Shannon
The protesters wave their banners in the breeze
But will the protesting people stop lives from being lost.

Triumphant

I am climbing Kilimanjaro
It is cold and wet
But still I am managing
It is hot and I am very tired
Sleep is what I need
But persevering
But when I go to sleep
I will never forget
The cold and dampness of Kilimanjaro
I will return triumphantly to Ireland
Having looked over Africa
From Kilimanjaro's heights.

2003 eurochild

Banners in the Breeze: Phillip Powell
Triumphant: James Wilmot
Art: Ben O'Conor

I Want to Be an Astronaut

I want to be an astronaut
I think I'll have to wait.
You have to be at least nine years old
And I am only eight.

Who Wants to Be
an Astronaut

I want to be an astronaut
And sail the world so high
I'd give them a wave here and there
Then I'd be king of the sky

2003 gyrochild

I Want to Be an Astronaut: Matthew Ahern
Who Wants to Be an Astronaut: Jamie Crowley
Art: Barry Wilson

The Twin Towers

If I could paint I'd show you
What happened on that day
The planes went headlong
On the streets of the USA
There was terrible confusion
As the towers came tumbling down
We won't forget that day
When Ground Zero got its name.

Twin Towers

If I could paint I'd show you
what happened on that day.
As I came in from school
I heard my mother say:
"The Towers, the Towers are crumbling
and one has fallen to the ground."
And as we watched closely the other one came down
"God help those little children and those parents left behind!"

2003 eurochild

The Twin Towers: Jerry Murphy
Twin Towers: Mícheál Crowley

Munster Rugby

When Munster played Gloucester
They had to win by 27
All the fans said
"If we do that, it will be like Heaven"
But we did it and we did it well
With the score being 33 to 6
Scoring tries, victory we could smell
When we kicked the ball between the sticks

The Madness of War

I really think,
The world has gone mad,
In America and Iraq,
There are thousands sad,
People are planning,
A World War Three,
Which doesn't sound good to me,
Bombing a country,
As small as Iraq,
Is definitely just
A madness attack!

eurochild
2003

Munster Rugby: Andrew Desmond
The Madness of War: Cian O'Donovan

Huff

I hate being in a huff
It makes me very mad
I get all cross and grumpy,
It makes me feel bad.

I lose all my friends
The loneliness hurts me a lot
My gloomy hearts burns
And is beginning to rot.

Please please forgive me
I am eager for friends again
I will write down a promise
With my gold and silver pen.

I value all of you a lot
I'll never again be so dense
Being so unforgiving
Just makes no sense.

2003 eurochild

Huff: Jonathan Taaffe
Art: Rebecca Geoghegan

My Mother

My mother died
I really cried
I think about her
My heart just floats down
When I'm sad.

My heart soars
When I think of good times
Like when she left
Me a Leeds jersey
On my chair as a surprise.

Life

Life is
Mystery
No one understands it
Only the people
Who have gone.

eurochild
2003

My Mother: Cian Collins
Life: Marco Quatrana

He was Homeless

He was very old
And very cold
He had no home
He was alone

He lived in a sewer
He was sick
There was no cure
For the man in the sewer

He was Homeless: Shane O'Neill
Art: Khatia Dzimistarishvili

War and Peace

War
Killing, shooting,
Explosions, slaughter,
Random, unexplained,
Terrifying, excruciating.

Peace
Slowly, halting,
Happiness, rejoicing,
Agreement, hugs,
Paradise, love.

War and Peace: Ian Quigley

War

I walked through the dark trenches,
Trying to decide
Whether I should run away,
Or whether I should hide.

I hated killing and fighting,
And I don't know why I went,
But all that I knew
Then was that,
My days were surely spent.

Machine guns fired
Behind me,
I was very, very afraid.
Then suddenly my
Lieutenant fell,
To this day I visit his grave.

The general of my squad,
Was stubborn to the end,
But when the war was ended,
His stubborness did mend.

War: Cian Dennehy
Art: Paul Stuchlik

The Beauty of the World

The beauty of the world makes me happy.
The blooming flowers.
The weeping willows.
The daisies in the grass.
All make me happy.

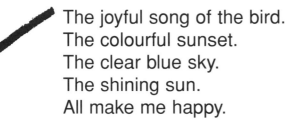

The joyful song of the bird.
The colourful sunset.
The clear blue sky.
The shining sun.
All make me happy.

I smile in awe at the
Wonderful things that surround me.
They are such beautiful sights.
I'm so happy that I have
The gift to see them all.

2003 eurochild

The Beauty of the World: Gillian O'Connell
Art: Christine Conroy

The Beauty of the World has Made me Happy

The beauty of the world has made me happy,
With the dawning of each new day.
And the sun will beam down
On the wet and cold ground
And the wet blades of grass will gleam.

I see this every day
The world always lets me say
There's a possiblity of change today.

Change rides on the wings of the wind
The wind blows through my hair, to bring
A possibility of change today.

2003

The Beauty of the World has Made me Happy: Rebekah Mahon

(146)

A Ballad
(When Cinderella met Sleeping Beauty)

One fine pleasant evening last summer,
I was strolling along the main street.
When two very strange looking people,
Suddenly happened to meet.
Now one was Cinderella, the other Sleeping Beauty.
They met that evening while heading,
Back to their fairytale duties

When they met in the street,
"Let's swap places" Beauty said.
"Alright" replied Cindy
"You can go to the ball,
And I'll stay in bed"
"Fine, while you sleep
I'll go to the ball instead"

After a week, I checked up on the swap,
Which sadly wasn't going well at all.
Poor Sleeping Beauty felt tired,
And didn't bother to go to the ball
The Prince who took badly to being stood up,
Said "This is the last straw, I've had enough".

eurochild
2003

A Ballad (When Cinderella met Sleeping Beauty): Sarah Petch

Light/Dark
A Memoriam/September 11, 2001

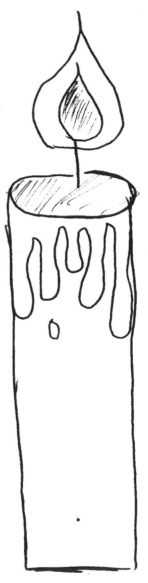

Light/Dark
The world went black,
Free then frightened,
Running scared.
Sirens screaming, rushing, racing.
Clouds of smoke swirled about.
Trapped - can't get out.

Victims of terror - each one,
Mother, father, daughter, son.
Policeman, Fireman never found,
Buried beneath the ground.
Every culture, every creed,
Very much remembered.

2003 eurochild

Light/Dark (A Memoriam/September 11, 2001): John O'Sullivan
Art: Joanne O'Sullivan

Newgrange

Newgrange is famous for its powerful light,
And magical shining rays,
But only on the winter solstice
Does the light shine that day.

With its standing stones outside it,
Standing solemn and quite still,
Just like 2000 years ago,
The druids busy at their quills.

Who knows what mysteries lie there,
We hope that they will do change,
The secrets are kept with the druids,
In the Boyne valley, in the tombs of Newgrange.

Newgrange: Fiona Finn

Voyage, Voyage

On voyage en car, en avion, en bateau...
On ne voyage pas sur les ailes d'un oiseau,
On voyages dans différents pays
Au Portugal ou l'Italie
Y'en a qui font des voyages sur la lune
Dans le désert, sur les dunes
Moi, je m'en vais au Portugal
Je mettrai mes souvenirs dans ma malle
Les voyages ne font pas de mal.

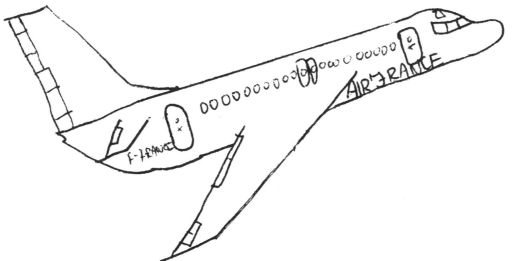

2003

Voyage, Voyage: Lola
Art: Shane Riordan

Halloween

Wicked witches soar the sky
Incantations eye to eye
Zany warlocks duel and die
And vampire bats hit the sky
Ranks of zombies, howling wolves
Don't be scared it's Halloween.

We're so Lucky

At home in my house
In my nice warm bed
Thinking
About all the children
Who don't even have a house
Who are wet, cold and starving
Then there's me here
in my warm bed, healthy,
With my family
And I think we're so lucky.

eurochild
2003

Halloween: Larry Leonard
We're so lucky: Evelyn Kimmage
Art: Erin McBride

The Seasons

In every spring, awake the flowers round and small,
All through the spring they grow and grow and grow so tall,
All the lambs come out and play their mothers watch and wait,
They have to make sure they're not a hungry fox's bait,
In summer children of all ages go out and enjoy the sun,
Spending every minute of every day outside is such fun.

In Autumn the sun's warmth starts to fade,
The playful morning tide brings with it a child's lonely spade,
Long walks through meadows wide,
Now winter approachs and it's starting to get dark outside,
Winter's here freezing we march off to school,
If only it was summer again we could sit out in the cool,
But we can't change the way of life,
Well at least God keeps us from all strife.
The End

2003 eurochild

The Seasons: Shauna Gallagher

L'Europe

La France et ses danses
La Belgique qui est très chic,
L'Espagne et ses poissons
L'Allemagne et ses camions,
Le Luxembourg et son argent,
Le Portugal et tous ses chants,
La Grèce et ses déesses,
La Suède et sa sagesse.

La Finlande et la Hollande,
L'Irlande et ses langues,
Avec l'Italie qui est jolie,
Et une portion de pays,
Voilà comment on la construit,
L'Europe d'aujourd'hui.

L'Europe: Maïlys Rebora
Art: Олимпиа Симопулу

Winter

Winter is the time of year, when frost and snow suddenly appear.
Icy roads make driving slow.
Everyone's wrapped up from head to toe.
Nights are longer. Days are short and cold.
Now the Christmas season is beginning to unfold.
Trees covered in decorations. Shop windows full of toys.
Eating turkey and Christmas Pud.
Selection boxes always taste good.
Schools are closed. It's holiday time.
I can stay up late - get up after nine.
Returning to school after the New Year.
Homework and hard work, no reason to cheer.
Winter will soon be going away, it's a seaason I love
I wish it could stay!

eurochild 2003

Winter: Andrea Bowdren

Sandy

I have a pet called Sandy
In the house he's ever so handy
With a zoom zoom zoom
He cleans up my room
So I treat him with a big box of candy.

The Spring

The flowers are blooming,
The weather is warmer,
The birds are busy,
And so is the farmer,
He's looking after the animals,
The calves and the lambs,
And the birds are coming back
From warmer lands.

2003 *eurochild*

Sandy: David Power
The Spring: Jack Hussey
Art: Kétnecan Melachvili

Winter

Winter mornings are so cold
I hate getting up when I am told
I'll stay in bed and snuggle up
And curl under my duvet like a little bug
But I know I have to go to school
And face the teacher and all her rules
But if it snows and the roads are bad
Then we can stay at home with Dad.

2003 eurochild

Winter: Kellie Fitzgerald

Amizade

A amizade
é algo que não se pode
comprar, vender ou trocar
só dar.

A amizade é
harmonia, paz, amor
sem cor, nem cheiro
mas com sabor.

A amizade não tem distinção,
pois vem do coração.
Vamos ajudar, é preciso
Vamos ao paraiso

A amizade não tem preço!

Amizade: Inès Lisboa

At School

Nothing at school is funny
They don't even pay us money
They expect us to work in school and at home
I wish my teacher would leave me alone!

School

Form a line
Stand up straight
Where's your bag
Why are you late?
Get an alarm clock
Set it for eight
Another day at school
Isn't it great!!

At School: Ciara Victory
School: David Cannon

(158)

Humpty's Downfall

Humpty Dumpty was really too small
To get to the top of the big tall wall.
Simple Simon tried to help
Little Miss Muffet gave a yelp.
Jack and Jill gave a loan of their pail
Little Bo Peep's sheep just wagged its' tail.
He got up so far
Let out a cry
To Little Jack Horner, still eating his pie.
He lost his balance, rocked to and fro,
Try to hold on, but had to let go.
He hit the ground
They all stared in shock
As Humpty's head hit a giant big rock.
All the King's soldiers that night did boast
Of having a supper of egg on toast.

2003 eurochild

Humpty's Downfall: Aileen O'Mahony

Birds

Birds
fly
so
high
in
the
sky
and
sing
in
morning
nice
and
soft
it
is
so
sweet
to
wake
up
to
a
bird
singing

eurochild

2003

Birds: Rebecca Casey
Art: Sarah Casey

Child of Europe

I am a child of Europe too
I go to school
And so do you.
I've had some operations,
That have kept me out of school.
But always, when I'm better
I think school is really cool.

Child of Europe: Catherine Hayes
Art: Carolyn O'Connell

Ireland

Ireland is my country
It's part of Europe too.
I'm proud to be from Ireland
If you lived here, so would you!
The grass is very green here
Because of all the rain.
But my Dad is a farmer
And he never does complain.
The daffodils are lovely,
In the Spring, especially.
We've calves just born
Last Saturday, they're nice
and cuddly.

eurochild
2003

Ireland: Patrick O'Connell
Art: Cian Adams Gibson

Valentine's Day

Valentine's day is about love, peace and happiness,
I got four cards for Valentine's Day,
I like someone in my class,
I have a card for him,
But I don't think he has a card for me.

Disobeying

I disobeyed my mum by going out
playing football and running about,
I felt sorry when I was a little late,
I had upset my mum by disobeying.
I went home and said that I was sorry,
And said that I will be good tomorrow.

Valentine's Day: Margaret Kiely
Disobeying: Diogo Santana

Christmas Night

A gentle breeze rattled the window panes
of my dark lonely room,
I'm the only resident,
the animals and plants long
for the rays of sun,
for it's Christmas Night.

White glistening flakes of joy
drop from the muddy murky clouds
the countryside is washed
in a blanket of shimmering snow
the forests whisper a silent poem
for it's Christmas Night.

The oaks dance and sway
in the fragile breeze
all is quiet, a robin singing
a joyful song broke the peace
around the
fields and forests,
the stars shine bright
it's Christmas Night.

2003 eurochild

Christmas Night: Redmond Clancy
Art: Oisín Dorgan

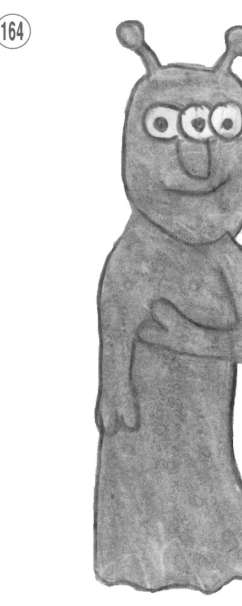

Up in Space

I'd like to fly up
into space and see
what lurks behind the
sky. With planets, stars,
moon and sun and
asteroids bumping up
and down.

Astronomers say there
might be life in
space
Is there?
I'd like to see for myself.

eurochild
2003

Up in Space: Emma Fitzgerald
Art: Emma Fitzgerald

A Button

Behold! A button am I
I am not the only button,
I have a small family and
I have no Mum or Dad,
I only have two brothers,
But don't forget my sister,
Nobody likes me,
Just because they're older than me,
They always bully me around.

My Dream

My name is Dean and this is my dream
To play for Liverpool like nobody has seen,
We will say goodbye to Roy Keane,
I'm new on the scene,
When he hears "Walk Alone" he will want to go home,
When I enter the field I hear the crowd scream
"Deano! Deano! You're the best on the team!"
So pack your bags Roy Keane,
I will shoot and score like never before,
Will they ever see someone better than Dean?

2003

A Button: Tony O' Reilly
My Dream: Dean Fitton

(166)

Silver Bird

Silver Bird, Silver Bird
What do you do?
I squeeze lemons just for you.

The Sea and the Sun

The sea and the sun are great fun,
They are loved by everyone,
The sun is hot,
The sea is cool,
I fish for shrimp in the sea pool,
The sun gives us a lovely tan,
Everyone visits the sea, even Gran!
We dig in the sand,
Make a castle and moat,
And Dad goes off on his sailing boat.

2003 *eurochild*

Silver Bird: Jennifer Hurley
The Sea and the Sun: Liam Reeves
Art: Stacy Walsh

Summer in Schull

Schull is the place for everyone,
For summer holidays
Where you'll have good fun.
Everyone's smiling,
The sun is shining.
See the crowds,
In the town,
At the beach
And in the park,
More are sailing on the sea,
Or fishing near the Carrig Lea,
Climb up Gabriel's hill so tall,
Hear the seagulls and curlews call.
Play some tennis, football, golf,
Come to Schull for the day,
You will love it in every way.

eurochild
2003

Summer in Schull: Lucy Hunt

Bonfire

The logs are piled up high
and the fire is burning
hotter and hotter.
The twigs start crackling.
They snap and fall
and ashes fly
everywhere.

The flames rise and
the logs
turn to amber
and change
shape and size.
What a beautiful sight
in the dark night!

Drinking hot chocolate.
Melting marshmallows.
Singing
camp-fire songs.
Getting cosy and warm
By the big bonfire.

eurochild
2003

Bonfire: Julien Bartolo Parnis
Art: Stacey Gallagher

Under the Sky

Under the sky,
There are lovely things,
Like trees,
And birds that fly,
And little kids who play,
Flying kites on a windy day.

Butterflies and pretty flowers,
Bumble bees collecting nectar,
Fish swimming in the sea,
All look wonderful to me.

Winter

White winter, snow on the roads,
In the chimney hear the breeze,
No one goes to the beach.
Thunder and lightning now and then.
Everyone waiting for the spring.
Ready, steady, go off winter.

Under the Sky: Aaron Carroll
Winter: Diarmuid O'Sullivan

Magic Days

Magic days are really fun,
Birthdays, Christmas, and Easter is one,
Magic days are for me and you,
And don't forget Halloween,
When we dress up really mean,
We laugh and sing and do lovely things,
Magic days make us happy,
Magic days live forever.

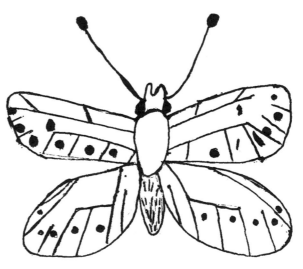

2003 eurochild

Magic Days: Shauna McSweeney
Art: Thomas O'Mahony

Santa

Santa is coming
And I can't go asleep
Nanny is snoring
The snow is falling
As Santa says "Ho! Ho! Ho!"

Christmas Night

S is for Santa who comes on Christmas Eve
A is for angel on top of the Christmas tree
N is for night-time when children are full of glee
T is for toys for you and me
A is for Aunties arriving for tea.

2003 *eurochild*

Christmas Night: David Bowes
Santa: Michael McCarthy
Art: Emma Fleury

Meeting in Hong Kong

Two dragons met in Hong Kong
which was told about in a song
as to how it all went wrong

They took each other by surprise
as one upon the other did rise

They fought for day and night
all was red and all was white

They ruined every nut and every grain
but soon it started to rain which
put out the flame,
ended the pain,
and they parted,
still alive, once again.

eurochild
2003

Meeting in Hong Kong: Peter Bain

The Funny Dog

The funny dog next door to us does
lots of funny things.
He chases cats, he chews
on mats, and runs around in rings.
He gets inside and eats the toys
and makes the children mad.
But because he is so small and cute
he's really not that bad.

The Funny Dog: Emer Fortune
Art: Katie O'Reily

Snow

I am covered with snow;
As you should know.
I am icy to touch.
I'm kind of like slush.
I am fat and round.
Although I see a lot around.
So I hope you know what I am?
I'm a very pretty snowman.

When temperatures fall; I still stand tall.
The snow around all melts about;
Not another snowflake comes to stay.
As the cold disappears; I begin to fold.
My nose just drops to the ground.
My arms and hands are also found.
The message is clear, as the sun is here.
I fear, I am running out of time.
The End

2003 eurochild

Snow: Aoibhín Ryan

Stars

Look at the skies tonight
And you will see
Everything and everyone
That's ever meant something to me.

If you don't understand right now
Don't worry, you will.
The moon, the stars,
The planets, the sun
Were once the souls of someone.

For every person that has died,
A new star appears in the sky.
For every ancient soul that's gone,
A new flame in the sun.

My granda, my cats
And everyone who has died,
New home now
Residing in the skies.

2003 eurochild

Stars: Saoirse Boyle
Art: Jillian Griffin

Peace

Peace is an action
Not just a word
But some people can't understand,
That peace is more important
Than money, than houses
Than power or even than land.

No matter what colour
Black or white,
Or what religion you are,
There's no need to argue,
Quarrel and fight,
Because peace is everyone's natural right.

2003 eurochild

Peace: Patrick Brogan

The Daft Dad

My Dad is called Bart
And kept darts in his butt
He fed his dog flower seeds
And kept cents in his nose
How daft he was!

My Father

He's always in a jolly mood,
with smiling eyes and a big wide grin.
I rarely hear him shout,
but he still likes discipline.
He loves his food
and thinks he's still slim.
With thinning hair and a full moustache,
he is quite handsome too.
My father's one in a million
and that's true!

2003 eurochild

The Daft Dad: Michael Apap Bologna
My Father: Luke Pellicano
Art: Daniel J.Maher

The Unicorn

The unicorn bolted and ran in the wild,
While the moon shone down, he left the circus behind.

His bright eyes flashed, as he rode on the wind,
He waded the river, but the light had turned dim.

Now he slowed down as he came to a wood,
Should he go in? Yes he must, yes we would!

But he was still wary, he got the feeling that,
Someone was watching, but who, but what?

And as he turned around. He got a surprise,
Another fair unicorn, with soft sky blue eyes.

Still they rode through the hills and they cantered together,
And as far as I know, they'll be riding forever.

2003 eurochild

The Unicorn: Marianne Kennedy

The Horse's Police Force

There was once a horse
who joined the police force.
It's a bit silly if I must say.
But hey! Petrol's a lot
dearer than hay.

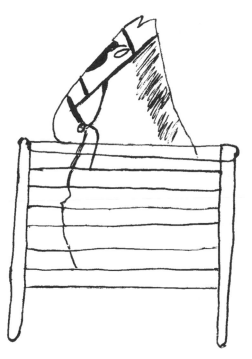

The Beach

I love the beach, it's nice and soft,
the sand, the sea,
the clouds, the sun
the view it's all for you.

2003

The Horse's Police Force: Kate Finnegan
The Beach: Shauna Ni Charthaigh-Crulai
Art: Tommy Kiely

In The Woods At Night

In the woods at night
You can get a fright
Freaky shadows, freaky trees
Makes you shake in your knees.

In the woods at night
You can get a fright
Rustling leaves on the ground
Like people walking all around.

In the woods at night
You can get a fright
Howling wolves, hooting owls
Squeaking bats and hissing cats.

In the woods at night
you can get a fright
Creaking branches like creaking doors
Makes you want to be inside doing chores.

2003 eurochild

In the Woods at Night: Aodhan O'Muirthile
Art: Jordan Lynch

Planets

There are nine planets in space,
May I name them all ?
There's Mercury closest to the sun,
Venus, same size as Earth,
Earth, isn't it the best?
Mars, it's bitter freezing nights,
Jupiter, giant of them all,
Saturn, three flat rings,
Uranus, trying to be like Saturn,
Neptune, better pack your bags,
165 years to get to the Sun,
Pluto, poor Pluto farthest and smallest of the nine,
So thats all nine!
You can thank me later!

2003

Planets: Megan O'Brien

I Hate Burgers

I hate burgers not like most
I think they're horrible and awfully gross.
I hate the lettuce, tomatoes and cheese,
But worst I think is the flat brown meat.

McDonald's is the place to go,
But if someone asks me I just say "no".
If someone says you'll really love it,
I turn away and have a chicken nugget.

eurochild
2003

I Hate Burgers: Dara Leong

Computers

Some computers are large,
some are little.
Some computers are tough,
some are brittle.

Some are blue,
some are red.
Some are good,
some are bad.

Some are fast,
some are slow.
Some stay in one piece
unless given a heavy blow!

Computers: Robert Attard
Art: Yanis Tonna

My Family

Daddy's name is Sam
He's a taxi man
Driving all day long
He sings a happy song.

Mammy is Fidelma
She works hard too
In the office all day long
Super Mum all the way.

Caolán is my brother
He is almost two
He gets around very fast
He is active to the last.

I am Sionnain
Seven years old
Is gaeilgeoir mé
I'm a dote, or so I'm told!

2003 eurochild

My Family: Sionnain Nic Eochaidh

Jamie The Dragon

There once was a girl called Amy.
She had a pet dragon called Jamie.
He used to eat creatures,
But now he eats teachers.
He burnt down a tree,
And drank the sea.
He spat on the town,
And made them all drown.
He stomped on the school,
And I thought it was cool.

And now that girl called Amy,
Still has her pet dragon Jamie.
He's as big as a steeple,
And he scares lots of people.

And one fine day,
In the month of May,
He scared poor Amy away.

eurochild
2003

Jamie The Dragon: Jessie Fraser
Art: Diogo Santana

Decisions, Decisions

The first kid president,
I'd like to be,
The first kid astronaut,
That could be me.

The first kid artist,
I could be that,
The first kid police cop,
I've my dress-up hat!

Maybe this, maybe that,
Maybe me, maybe perhaps.

I could be anything,
Anything I could be,
Maybe a kid,
Is what I should be.

Decisions, Decisions: Brittany Nicole Wilson

Prayer of a Shark

Dear God, give us
enough fish to eat
and let there be no more
rubbish thrown in the sea.
Let all people be my friends.
Amen.

2003

Prayer of a Shark: Luke Aquilina
Art: Yasmyn Safar Hamidi

Fog

Strange, thick, twirling
massive white or grey,
Coming towards me swirling
circling trees on the way.

Looking out the window
nothing I can see
except one big grey shadow
that looks like a soupy sea.

Over the mountainland down the hill
all the way to the peaty bog
swallowing even the mile
strange and spooky is the fog.

Fog: Alannah Ganly

The Tooth Fairy

I lost my first tooth when I was five,
It was a big surprise.

Put it under your pillow,
Was my Mum's advice.

I tossed and turned all night long,
And in the morning I found

The Tooth-fairy had left,
A lovely shiny pound.

A Power Boat

A power boat is an amazing invention
The way it ploughs through the water
like a bulldozer through sand.
And the roar from the engine
like a tiger at it's prey.

eurochild
2003

The Tooth Fairy: Aileen O'Mahony
A Power Boat: Michael McCarthy
Art: Michael McCarthy

Games

I love games they're lots of fun
Many boring people think they're dumb
Games are nice to relax and play
Just switch on the power and enjoy the day
Why not play X-box or Playstation 2
There is always room for Gameboy too.
You could play *Super Mario* or *Pokemon* aswell,
Where your next adventure goes you never can tell,
You can adventure as Frodo in *Lord of the Rings*,
In games you can do so many things.

2003

Games: Paul Stuchlik

Time

The time is going
The night is showing
The river is flowing
The moon is glowing
The cat prowls
The wolf howls
The dawn arrives
The world's alive

World be Happy

Dear God up in Heaven
who watches and makes me so happy,
happy as can be,
I know there's many children
who are sad and lonely as their
country is fighting over many different things,
So please God up in Heaven
hear this my little prayer,
Please make all children happy everywhere.

2003 eurochild

Time: Ciara Halpin
World be Happy: Mark Murphy
Art: Mantai Balairi

192

Leaves

Leaves on the brown ground
Falling from up, up, up high,
Littering the ground,
Soundlessly falling downwards,
Landing lightly on our heads.

Moving House

Last year, July
I moved from Dublin
It was difficult
But in fact
I have more friends
Than before
It was good in the end
Or was it...?

2003 eurochild

Leaves: Laurence McCarthy
Moving House: Maggie Mac Aonghusa

The Sleepy Cat

He opens his sleepy eyes,
Stands up and arches his back.
He stretches his mouth open
And yawns!
He lowers his back,
and quietly walks
about his business
until yet again
The cat is asleep.

The Sleepy Cat: Denise Burns
Art: Fiachra Ó Corragáin

eurochild
2003

194

Náramek přátelství

Náramek přátelství pro tebe mám,
Nevím však, zda-li ti ho dám.
Jsi daleko ode mne, lásko má,
Avšak v srdci svém tě stále mám.
Na dvoře stojím a myslím na tebe,
Jsi láska má, já nevzdám se tě.

Dostaneš červený, co lásku znamená.

Červený náramek jediný mám,
a jenom tobě ho dám.
Modrý dostane můj dobrý kamarád,
protože mě nemá jako ty rád.
Růžový své mamince dám,
Od ní to bohatství mám.

Zelený dostane můj milý tatínek,
To on mi dal první zlatý prstýnek.
Tyto kouzelné náramky mám
A jen těmto lidem je dám.

2003 eurochild

Náramek Prátelství: Marie Paulicková

In The Summer

In the summer when I go to bed
The sun still streaming overhead
My bed becomes so small and hot
With sheet and pillows in a knot
And then I lie and try to see
The things I'd really like to be.

I think I'd be a West Highland Terrier
There'd be no dog that was merrier
I'd get my own back on the cat
And chase him off his comfy mat.

I think I'd be a guinea-pig
Running around in a hutch so big
I wouldn't let anything get in my way
Of eating lettuce non-stop all day.

eurochild
2003

In The Summer: Kerry O'Shea

Bed-Timers

A minute to nine o' clock and I'm in bed
I begin to hear the world outside,
I see shadows, I hear the sound of birds
setting down for the night
a plane sweeping through the sky,
I catch a shadow in the corner of my eye,
I'm scared.

And these things I think about,
how cosy and warm it is to be here,
I feel safe under the covers,
I'm as safe as can be,
I peep my head out the side of the sheets,
I'm scared.

A minute to nine, and I'm still up!
I wish I could go to sleep,
I begin to count sheep, 1,2,3, I'm bored,
I shut my eyes and rest my head,
its so great to be in my bed,
I'm scared.

And these things I think, my eyes are heavy,
I want to stay to stay awake,
to hear the sound of my mum and dad,
I'm asleep.

eurochild
2003

Bed-timers: Matthew Selby
Art: Christine Conroy

A Minute to Nine

A minute to nine o'clock and I'm in bed
There are lots of noises that I can hear
Cats are fighting on our front wall
Next door's dog barking at the phone
The wind rustling around our trees
The greenhouse windows rattling
All the street lights flickering.

And these things I think
I can see around my room:
My posters of pop singers come alive
My CDs start to dance
My clock starts ticking to the beat
Clothes come out of my wardrobe and do a catwalk
My teddy does the can-can

A minute to nine and I'm still up
I think I need to go to bed later
I want to watch TV
Because I'm hot and bored
I wish I would be able to go to bed when I like
Because being in bed is not so great !

And these things I think
To fly away to a different galaxy
Where I can be my favourite actress
Or be a funky popstar
But right now I'm tired and bored, so it's time to sleep.

A Minute to Nine: Louise Wadsworth
Art: Louise Roche

Dán a Scríobh? Ní Féidir Liom!

Tá mo pheann luaidhe briste,
Níl scriosán agam,
Tá mo pháipéar uafásach,
Ní thaitníonn sé liom.

Tá pian i mo bholg,
Tá pian i mo cheann,
Tá an-craic sa ghairdín,
Ba mhaith liom bheith ann.

Tá na héiníní ag canadh,
Tá an madra ina luí,
Is mise ag obair,
Gan athas, gan spraoi.

Nach dtuigeann tú,
Duirt me riamh,
Ní féidir liom,
Dán a scriobh!

Dán a Scríobh? Ní Féidir Liom!: Oisín Ó Corragáin

The Special Olympics

Who will win
Who will lose.
It's not up to us.

They start to run
in the sun.
They all wonder,
who'll be the one.

The time has come
to see who won,
But most of all
they had some fun.

June 2003

Usually they are held in the States
But for the first time they are held in Ireland.

All of us will rejoice when June comes,
So go and watch these determined people
As they fight their disability.

The Special Olympics: Katie Jennings
June 2003: Aishling Ní Eanna

2003 eurochild

Index of Poets and Artists

2003 *eurochild*

Schools Index

2003 eurochild

Submissions are invited for
Eurochild 2004

Write to:
Eurochild 2004
Tigh Filí
Thompson House
MacCurtain Street
Cork, Ireland
Phone: + 353 21 4509274
Email:admin@cwpc.ie
Web: www.tighfili.com

Pour la compétition
Eurochild 2004 veuillez envoyer
vos poémes et vos dessins

á l'adresse suivant:
Eurochild 2004
Tigh Filí
Thompson House
MacCurtain Street
Cork, Ireland
Phone: + 353 21 4509274
Email:admin@cwpc.ie
Web: www.tighfili.com

2003 *eurochild*